EVERYMAN'S
WILD FLOWERS AND TREES

EVERYMAN'S WILD FLOWERS AND TREES

Five hundred of the British wild flowers, trees, shrubs, grasses, and ferns, described and illustrated, 384 in colour after Sowerby's *British Wild Flowers*, and 120 from line - drawings by the Author

BY MILES HADFIELD

LONDON
J · M · DENT & SONS LTD
NEW YORK: E · P · DUTTON AND COMPANY INC.

PREFACE

THE aim of this book is to illustrate and describe the plants, trees, shrubs, grasses, and ferns most noticeable, either because of their frequency or outstanding appearance, to the ordinary person — or Everyman—living in the British Isles, and particularly to draw attention to their uses, garden or cultivated relatives, and any other interesting associations they may have, regarding them not as specimens to be identified and labelled, but as integral parts of the natural world, and often of civilization also.

The use of the beautiful drawings by J. E. Sowerby in *British Wild Flowers*, an old book which deservedly went through many editions in its day, now reproduced for the first time by modern methods, has made possible the coloured illustration of no less than 384 plants in this one small volume. It has also made possible the selection of drawings to suit the text, which has not (as is so often the case) been written around an existing incomplete set of figures. The line-drawings are restricted to those plants not shown by Sowerby, and to the commonest kinds of all. In them an opportunity has been taken to show interesting features missed in casual observation.

Most books such as this are restricted to our truly native plants, but 'the poverty of the British flora is due to the Ice Age . . . but the Ice Age is now a thing of the past,' [1]—and many of the plants brought over by our conquerors to supply food, drugs, or even accidentally, and of the innumerable kinds introduced since to our gardens, woodlands, and parks, have liked the land of their adoption so well that they have become *naturalized* without the further help of man. These foreigners are called *exotic* as opposed to *native* plants.

We look, too, upon the golden-flowered laburnum and the horse-chestnut as typical of the British scene, yet neither is native, and Shakespeare probably never saw a horse-chestnut in flower. But these, with many such plants, have been included, though often omitted from larger books.

The wide range covered by this book has been made possible by attempting to select those plants that it is *probable* the reader will notice when out for a walk in the country, on his seaside holiday, or even when weeding his garden (there is plenty of interest in this).

[1] *British Trees and Shrubs*, H. Gilbert-Carter, 1936.

Features of the modern landscape rich in wild flowers are the golf-links, the waste land around building developments, and the railway embankment, where seed blown on to the trains in one district are often deposited miles away in another by a sudden draught or wind.

If the reader becomes seriously interested in plant-life, he will realize that this, or, indeed, any book, only touches the fringe of a vast subject with many branches. General books of a comprehensive and intelligible type, which have been frequently consulted by the author, and, as they should be on the shelves of any good library, are recommended to the reader, are: Bentham and Hooker's *Handbook of the British Flora* (seventh edition, revised by A. B. Rendle, 1930), with its companion volumes, *Illustrations of the British Flora* by Fitch and others and *Further Illustrations of British Plants* by Butcher and Strudwick. These are the standard works of their kind, but are rather inadequate concerning trees, and the reader is therefore referred to *Trees and Shrubs Hardy in the British Isles* by W. J. Bean (3 vols., 1914–33) and *The Identification of Trees and Shrubs* by F. K. Makins (1936). For modern systems of classification and general information *A Dictionary of the Flowering Plants and Ferns* by J. C. Willis (1931), and for names and terms, *A Popular Dictionary of Botanical Names and Terms* by G. F. Zimmer (third impression) should be consulted, while for the economic and agricultural uses of plants, *Agricultural Botany* by J. Percival (latest edition), and the appropriate publications of the Royal Botanic Gardens, Kew, the Ministry of Agriculture and Fisheries, and the Forests Products Research Laboratory are valuable authorities.

Other useful works are: *British Ferns and their Varieties* by C. T. Druery (1910), *The Gramineae* by Agnes Arber (1934), and *British Grasses* by S. F. Armstrong (1937). Certain others are mentioned in the text.

I have to thank a friend, who wishes to remain anonymous, for valuable suggestions and criticisms.

It should be remembered that our wild flowers are the common heritage of all, and that careless and reckless picking of flowers and branches, particularly if done in the name of nature study, is indefensible and may do much harm to the plants we like.

M. H.

CONTENTS

CHAPTER I

THE PARTS OF A PLANT

As this book deals primarily with the identification and naming of plants we may pass over such subjects as their life-histories and functions[1] and concern ourselves solely with a short description of such of their parts as are necessary for our purpose.

Nearly all the plants mentioned in this book have two distinct systems, one, consisting mostly of the *root*, underground (or, in some aquatic plants, submerged in the water) which absorbs the necessary plant foods and water; the other aerial and including the *stem*, the *leaves*, and the *flowers*.

A plant may be an *annual*, when the seed germinates and develops into a complete plant which flowers and bears seeds and then dies all within one year; a *biennial* when, during its first year, it produces above ground leaves only (often in a rosette or tuft), and in its second flowers and seeds in addition, after which effort it dies; or a *perennial* when it produces flowers and seeds over a number of years (although not always every year), not dying as a matter of course at the end of the second. Perennials vary greatly in length of life from three or four years in some plants (not necessarily small) to several centuries in the case of an oak-tree, for example.

Root and Rootstock

The *root* consists usually of a number of fibres in close contact with the earth. Some plants have a *tap-root*, a long, thick, central root driving deeply into the soil with rootlets branching off it. Others have fibrous roots alone, often growing in tufts from the joints of the stem when these take the form of long, thin *runners* lying flat on the ground.

Most plants possess a *rootstock*. This is classed as part of the stem, but may be regarded as intermediate between that and the root. If a stinging nettle is pulled up, the part just under the ground will be found to consist of pinkish stems, mostly running parallel with the surface of the ground, bearing roots at each joint. These stems are not the real roots, which are the tufts at the joints, but the *rootstock*, in

[1] For an introduction to these see *Botany*, J. Reynolds Green, 1924.

this case called *rhizomes*. (The rhizome is also well illustrated in the flag and bearded irises of gardens.)

If the rootstock is very swollen in parts (the swelling accumulates a store of food) it is said to be *tuberous*; a fine example of such a *tuber* is seen in the potato.

Other forms of the modified stem or rootstock are the *bulb* and the *corm*. They provide shelter for the plant when it is dormant, and food supplies to help it into growth. Each produces a tuft of roots at its base and leaves and flowers from its tip when in growth. When they die at the end of the season these can be removed without harm to the plant. A *bulb* consists of a series of overlapping scales, a *corm* is firm and solid throughout.

THE STEM

The stem proper is *herbaceous* (in which case the plant is a *herb*), when it is soft and not woody above ground, usually dying back each year to the rootstock.

In trees and shrubs the stem is hard and *woody*; it does not normally die back, but bears fresh shoots along it each year.

A *shrub* is generally defined as a woody plant without a clear trunk and branched down to the ground, under 30 ft. high.

A *tree* is a woody plant which develops a clear trunk or bole carry- ing a head of branches, over 30 ft. high.

A tree or shrub is *deciduous* when the leaves fall annually, *evergreen* when the leaves fall more irregularly after they have been on the plant several years. Therefore the plant is always more or less covered with leaves.

THE LEAF, PLATE I

The leaf consists of a *blade* (*t*) which may be almost any shape. It is often carried on a *leaf-stalk* (*u*) attached to the stem, which may be quite long or so short that it is almost non-existent, when it is said to be *sessile* (this also applies to flowers and flower-stalks). In the angle between the stem and the leaf-stalk, called the *axil* (*x*) buds (embryo shoots, leaves, or flowers) are usually produced. If the leaf springs from the rootstock, it is called *radical*.

The leaf is built round what are popularly known as *veins*. These are usually arranged on one of three plans: *pinnately* (A), like a feather; *palmately* (B), like the fingers spreading from the palm; or *parallel* (C). The leaf edge may be smooth and *entire* (Text Fig. 270), *toothed* (Text

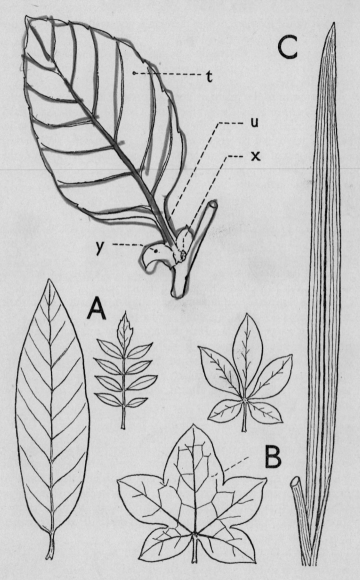

PLATE I—THE LEAF

Fig. 112) in several fashions, or more deeply divided into *lobes*. Some-times it is very deeply cut or *dissected* (Text Fig. 172). The terms pinnate and palmate have the same meaning applied to these divisions of the leaf.

Such leaves are *simple*; when the divisions are so deep that they reach the central rib, and each division is on a little stalk of its own, the leaf is called *compound*, and is composed of separate *leaflets*. Here again the words palmate and pinnate are applied to the different arrangements (see Text Figs. 84 and 104 respectively).

Often a pair of leaf-like growths, called *stipules* (y), are found at the base of the leaf-stalk, not infrequently falling as the leaf develops.

The Flower, Plates II and III

The flower is generally regarded as the interesting part of a plant, and is most frequently used as the means of its identification.

It is usually carried on a *flower-stalk*, either singly or in clusters. Such clusters are called an *inflorescence* (see page 6). Protective leaflets are often present on these stalks, and are called *bracts* (b^1).

A usual type of flower consists of a greenish-coloured outer casing, forming the enclosing bud in the early stages, called the *calyx*. This is indicated by s throughout the figures in this book. It may be divided into distinct segments called *sepals*, or else it is somewhat tubu-lar in shape, dividing into lobes or teeth. More rarely it is coloured and petal-like. Inside the calyx is the *corolla* (p), which is often brightly coloured to attract the attention of insects. The corolla may consist of *petals* either separate or joined at their base; or be tubular in shape, dividing into lobes. Some of the typical arrangements of petals are shown on Plates II and III. The calyx and corolla together form the *perianth*. It is often difficult to divide the perianth into a distinct calyx and corolla, particularly in monocotyledonous plants (page 144). The two are then spoken of simply as the perianth.

Inside the perianth are the *stamens*. Each is composed of a stalk or *filament* attached at its base to the flower, and bearing at its free end the *anther* (an) which is coated with pollen. This may be regarded as the male part of the flower. In the centre of the flower is the *pistil* or *gynaeceum* or female part. It consists of one or more *carpels*, which may be separate or fused together into one. Each carpel consists of an *ovary* (o) at its base, which is a chamber containing the unfertilized seeds or *ovules*; it is then usually elongated into a *style* which terminates in a *stigma* (st). The flower is, so to speak, built up on the *receptacle*.

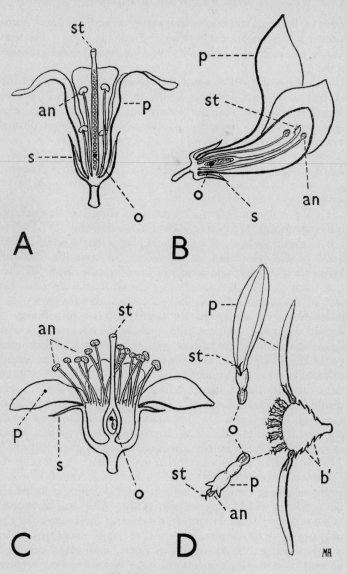

PLATE II—THE FLOWER

The type of flower described is complete or *hermaphrodite*, that is it includes both male and female parts. Not infrequently a plant bears these organs in separate male and female flowers, the male producing pollen and the female seed. These separate male and female flowers may be mixed on the same plant, which is then called *monoecious*, or they may be distinct on separate plants, which are then *dioecious*.

To produce fertile seed the pollen must be transferred from the anther to the stigma. This is usually done by bees, flies, or other insects clambering about the flower to collect or sip the sweet nectar it often contains, although pollen itself is collected by bees. Catkin-bearing plants and grasses are among those whose pollen is transferred by the wind. Unfortunately, lack of space has made it impossible to mention details of pollination in the descriptions below.

THE FRUIT

The ovules fertilized, they develop. The petals and other now useless parts often fall, and the carpels enlarge to protect the *fruit*. It should be emphasized that a fruit is not something edible, but the covering of the seed. There are several types. The *capsule* when ripe consists of several dry, skinny cells, from which the seeds are liberated by the splitting of *valves* or the opening of *pores*. In a *berry* the seed is enclosed by a skin, which is embedded in a fleshy mass, in its turn enclosed by a skin (e.g. a gooseberry). Many fruits often called berries are not strictly speaking so. Often they are *drupes* (e.g. a cherry) which have the seed enclosed in a hard shell—the 'kernel' inside the 'stone'—which is also surrounded by a fleshy mass enclosed by a skin. The *nut* has the seed enclosed by a woody covering; the *achene*, often looking like the seed itself, has a leathery covering. Excepting the capsule, all these liberate the seed by the rotting of the outer layers. Other fruits are described in the descriptions below.

THE INFLORESCENCE, PLATE IV

The *inflorescence* consists of a number of flowers arranged on a main axis. There are many types, but the following are the most important:

Spike (Fig. A) (page 9). The flowers stalkless, arranged more or less closely along the main axis.

Raceme (Fig. B). The flowers are carried on stalks more or less equal in length along the main axis.

Corymb (Fig. C). Flower-stalks from the main axis are of unequal length, so that the flowers are more or less all on the same level.

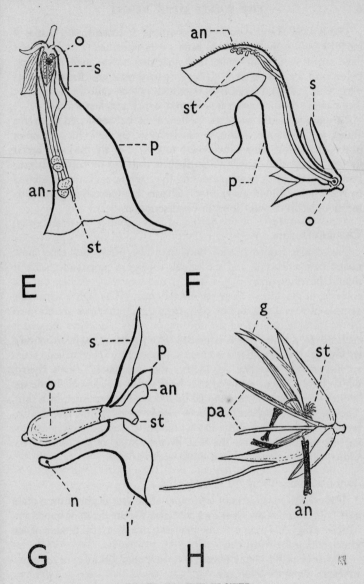

PLATE III—THE FLOWER

Panicle (Fig. D). A *compound inflorescence* consisting of a series of racemes carried along the main axis.

Umbel (Fig. E). The main axis terminated in a series of flower-stalks of more or less equal length. In a *compound umbel* (Text Fig. 171) these flower-stalks bear instead of flowers another umbel.

A *cyme* (Fig. F) is variable in appearance (one example is shown in Text Fig. 296), but is formed in the following manner: the main axis produces a flower and stops growing at its tip, but some little way down forms a secondary stem which again terminates in the production of a flower. In its turn, this bears another similar (this time, tertiary) stem with its flower, and so on.

A *catkin* is a form of spike, usually, but by no means always, hanging, and generally including flowers of one sex only.

The inflorescences of the daisy and grass families are described in Chapter II below.

CHAPTER II

FLOWER TYPES (Plates II and III)

THE structure of the typical flowers of some of the most abundant families are here described.

WALLFLOWER FAMILY (page 28). Fig. A (page 5). Four separate petals form a cross, enclosed by a calyx of four sepals. Stamens, six, four long and two short. Carpels, two, united.

PEA FAMILY (page 48). Fig. B. The five sepals are united at the base. The five petals are separate. One is large and more or less erect, called the *standard*; two, one at each side, form the *wings*; while two below are interlocked on their lower edge by hairs, and are called the *keel*, enclose the single carpel with its stigma, which is surrounded by ten stamens, usually united to form a tube.

ROSE FAMILY (page 54). Fig. C. The receptacle forms a cup, somewhat variable in shape, on the rim of which are attached the sepals, usually either four or five; the petals, either four, five, or rarely none; and the stamens, generally very numerous. The number of carpels varies from one to several (see Text Fig. 121).

DAISY FAMILY (page 84). Fig. D. More accurately an inflorescence than a type of flower. Taking the daisy as a type, the receptacle is short and flat or conical, surrounded by a whorl of small bracts.

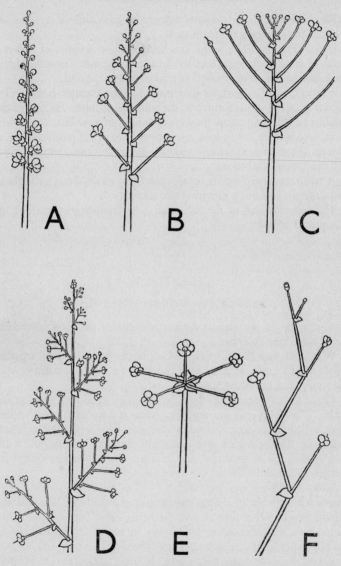

PLATE IV—THE INFLORESCENCE

Around the outer rim is a *ray* of florets. This consists of a short tube enclosing a pistil and opening out to form a single white petal. The yellow centre, or *disk*, consists of closely packed tubular florets each containing pistil and anthers. The calyx of the individual florets in this family is represented by a small bract or bristle at their bases.

The flower-head varies on both sides of this type from one in which all the florets are tubular (No. 228) to one in which the florets are all strap-shaped, of the ray type (No. 248).

FIGWORT FAMILY (page 114). Fig. E. Calyx usually with four segments, often sharp teeth, which remain around the fruit. The corolla in one piece opening out into four or five lobes, often forming two lips. Stamens, two or four, rarely five, attached to the tube of the corolla.

LABIATE FAMILY (page 120). Fig. F. Calyx tubular, usually with five teeth. Corolla tubular, opening into four or five lobes and often forming two lips (Latin, *labium,* lip). Stamens, two or four. Ovary deeply divided into four.

ORCHID FAMILY (page 149). Fig. G. Perianth with six petal-like segments, three outer (*s*), and three inner (*p*), one of which forms the *lip* (*l¹*). What appears to be a flower-stalk is a long ovary, terminating in the *column.* This is formed of the united stamens and stigma. Its upper tip is the equivalent of the anther, while the lower side of the projecting *beak* is the stigma. The long spur is the *nectary* (*n*).

GRASS FAMILY (page 161). Fig. H. The flowers are in spikelets, and are enclosed in bract-like *glumes* (*g*). The lower pair are usually empty; the upper, the *flowering glumes*, contain the anthers and the small feathery stigma. In the example shown the flower nearest the top of the page is hermaphrodite, that below is staminate only. The glumes often bear long bristles or *awns*. The two scales marked *pa* in the centre of the flower are called *palea*.

CHAPTER III

HOW PLANTS ARE CLASSIFIED AND NAMED

IT is not necessary to define here what is meant by a plant, but it must be remembered that such a definition will have to include both the huge almost primeval forest trees of N. America and the green scum floating on a pool. It will be more to our purpose to show how this vast

mass of material is classified and named by a system which is understood by any trained botanist, whatever his nationality.

If we take a gorse flower and compare it with that of a laburnum we
shall find that they are both formed on the same pattern. Later in
the year, the flower of a sweet pea shows a similar structure. Yet one
is a shrub, one a tree, and the other a climbing plant.

A similar likeness of structure will be found in the flowers of the
wild rose and apple, though not so close in this case (they must be
memorized or sketched as they do not bloom simultaneously). Here
one is a thorny shrub and the other a cultivated tree. But flowers of
the rose and the apple are totally different from those of the gorse,
laburnum, and sweet pea.

These likenesses and dissimilarities give us the clue to the system of
plant classification. By comparing the structures of different plants,
particularly their flowers, the scientist is soon able to separate them into
groups, which he may further sub-divide, regardless of whether they
are annuals, perennials, trees, shrubs, arctic, or tropical plants. So the
gorse, laburnum, and sweet pea are collected in the pea family, the rose
and apple in the rose family.

The first big division that can be made is to separate those plants
which flower from those that do not. These divisions are called
Phanerogams and Cryptogams respectively. They are further sub-
divided according to the table below, the divisions being described at
the appropriate places in the text.

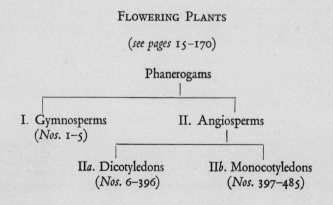

FLOWERING PLANTS

(*see pages* 15–170)

Phanerogams

I. Gymnosperms   II. Angiosperms
(*Nos.* 1–5)

              IIa. Dicotyledons   IIb. Monocotyledons
              (*Nos.* 6–396)   (*Nos.* 397–485)

Flowerless Plants

(see pages 170–75*)*

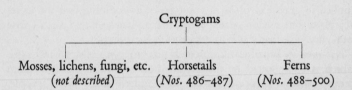

Cryptogams

Mosses, lichens, fungi, etc.	Horsetails	Ferns
(not described)	*(Nos.* 486–487*)*	*(Nos.* 488–500*)*

It is true that we are skipping certain sub-divisions recognized by modern botanists, but their inclusion would only complicate a book of this nature.

We next come to the families, sometimes called the natural orders. These may be regarded as the most useful unit for the identification of plants, the resemblances being generally sufficiently close, and at the same time sufficiently distinguishable, for the beginner to place their members without wading through a mass of detail. The families are eventually divided into *genera* (singular, *genus*) which are composed finally of *species*. So that a family has numerous members, its genera are fewer, while there is only one species.

But, particularly as we know more of plants, it is difficult to draw these hard and fast rules in so arbitrary a manner, and although we shall do so, it is as well to realize that nature does not. For instance, two distinct species, even genera, may interbreed, producing offspring unlike their parents, which are called *hybrids*, often of great importance in horticulture and agriculture. Again, in nature a great deal of variety may occur among the members of a group of one species, and it is often difficult to decide whether we have not in reality more than one species. If botanists are agreed that we have no justification for creating a new species, it is quite likely that they may define certain marked forms as *sub-species*, or more probably as *varieties* of the species. Varieties also are prominent in cultivation, varying from the typical species in some way of value to man.

PLANT NAMES [1]

Native plants have long had excellent British names, often with numerous local variants. In these are often found the old word *wort*,

---

[1] For a practical account of this, see *The Naming of Plants,* V. Higgins, 1937.

which was more or less the equivalent of the modern *plant*, though it appears to have been most frequently used in connection with medicinal plants. *Lily* and *rose* were often applied to plants with superficially lily-like and rose-like flowers; *grass*, too, was a wide term, not always applied to grass-like plants. *Cress* generally indicates that the leaves of a plant were used in salads; *horse-*, that a plant so called was a coarse form; and *dog-* that it was as common as were dogs.

But even in Britain confusion of names arises (see Nos. 86 and 259), which is complicated by the introduction of foreign plants without British names. Hence botanists, and indeed many other people, generally prefer to use the scientific rather than the popular name of a plant. It should be understood that a species has only one valid botanical name, though botanists being human, and botany being an ancient, as well as a progressive science, it may be known under several names; all except the correct one are *synonyms*.

The botanical name of a plant consists of the name of its genus, treated as a Latin noun, qualified by the name of the species, nearly always regarded as a Latin adjective, as often as not descriptive of some quality of the plant.[1] Thus we have *Juniperus communis*, which means the common species of the genus *Juniper*. Similarly, *Trollius europaeus* is the European trollius. These two names identify any recognized species. A variety is indicated by adding its name to the other two, prefixing it with *var*. The name of the genus always bears a capital initial, the name of the species never, unless it is (*a*) named after a person, more usual with recently discovered plants, e.g. the gentian, discovered by Reginald Farrer, *Gentiana Farreri*, (*b*) the ancient name of a plant or genus, not now used, except for a specific name, as in *Ranunculus Ficaria*, *Ficaria* being an old plant-name. In the U.S.A. these capitals are dropped.

Some Notes on Pronunciation

As all names are Latinized (though many are of Greek origin, and must be treated accordingly) the normal Latin pronunciation should be used. That is, every syllable must be pronounced, the one marked with an accent being stressed. Thus *arvénse* is three syllables, *ar-vén-se*, the second one being accented. It should be remembered that *ch* is pronounced hard, like *k*; *pt* simply as *t*; *cn* as *n*; while *ae* and *oe* are diphthongs and may be regarded simply as *e*. The termination *ii* is

[1] It should be mentioned that sometimes, for a variety of reasons, this descriptive adjective may be obscure or even wrong in its application.

one syllable, pronounced as a long *i*. When a personal name is used it is pronounced in the usual manner, with the Latin termination added, *Douglas-ii*.

NOTE.—To avoid confusion to the beginner the sequence of the description is, in general, that of Bentham and Hooker's *Handbook of the British Flora*, and its companion volumes, as experience has shown that these are the most usual standard works in public libraries. The division into families and nomenclature have been altered to conform with modern British publications of an official character (e.g. recent Kew Hand-lists).

The *Family* is first described at a length dependent on its importance in Britain, followed by the individual *species* of its *genera*. Any notes applying to a genus as a whole are placed at the end of the last species described. The order followed in the description of a species is: English name in capitals, botanical name followed by a translation of the specific name in italics, the usual period of flowering, and then botanical features and other notes. Neither the generic nor specific name is translated if it be the ancient name without different meaning or of obscure origin. The specific name is not translated when an old generic or personal name.

The text has been regarded as complementary to the illustrations, and any point, such as colour or leaf-shape, made clear in the figure is not repeated in the description, which aims at mentioning the salient points alone.

In the line figures, all insets (unless stated) are on an enlarged scale to the main figure. Flower sections are all longitudinal, i.e. cut *along* the stem, not across it. This lettering is used throughout: *s*, calyx; *p*, petal or corolla (or when calyx and corolla are combined, perianth); *st*, stigma; *an*, anther; b^1, bract; *g*, glume; *o*, ovary; *f*, fruit; *so*, sori.

CHAPTER IV

FLOWERING PLANTS

Phanerogams

PLANTS having flowers containing anthers, pistils, etc. and producing seed.

I. GYMNOSPERMS

Plants with the seeds naked (Greek, *gymnos*, naked, and *sperma*, seed), that is, unenclosed by a fruit.

They were more numerous in prehistoric times than to-day, and include the cycads, the lowest form of flowering plant now existing, resembling tree-ferns in appearance; the ginkgo or maidenhair-tree which, it is said, might now be extinct if not cultivated by the Chinese and Japanese (it is grown also in Britain); and the cone-bearers or *Coniferae*.

The conifers are usually evergreen trees or shrubs of pyramidal form, with leaves either needle-shaped, narrow and flat, or small and scale-like (see Text Figs. 5, 1, and 2 respectively). Male and female flowers are usually separate in an inflorescence consisting of a number of scales which enclose the flowers proper. After fertilization by wind, the scales of the female inflorescence enlarge, protecting the seed (but not enclosing it as a true fruit) and form the cone, a process often requiring several years to complete. When eventually the seed is ripe, it may either be blown or fall from between the scales, or the cone itself may fall and gradually break up.

Conifers grow typically in dense forests, unmixed with other trees, often (particularly in the tropics) among mountains. Parts of Europe, Asia, and N. America (particularly the Pacific coast) have huge areas of these forests, usually of ancient origin. In Britain, although we have fossilized remains of prehistoric conifers (including a tree similar to the giant wellingtonia), there are to-day only three native kinds, but no class of tree has been so widely introduced and planted for economic and ornamental purposes. Several kinds produce good timber in situations to which our native trees are unsuited. The timber of conifers is known commercially (not always with literal justification) as 'softwood.' The trees and timber usually contain resin.

It is the continuous shade, not any poisonous quality of the fallen needles, that prevents undergrowth in coniferous woods.

YEW FAMILY: *Taxáceae*

1. Yew, *Táxus baccáta, berried.* Early spring.

An evergreen tree, rounded when old, very hardy, and reaching a great age. The male flowers (figured growing among the leaves and

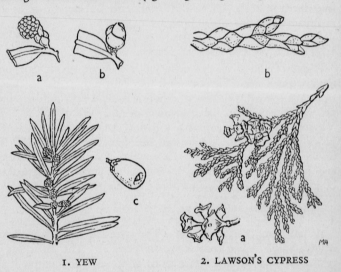

1. YEW   2. LAWSON'S CYPRESS

enlarged at *a*) and the female flowers (inset *b*) are yellowish-coloured, and grow normally on separate trees. A red fleshy 'berry' protects the seed instead of the usual cone (inset *c*). The timber was used for the bow and was of great importance, but is now valueless. All parts of the tree should be regarded as poisonous to man and beast, clippings from hedges particularly so to stock. The Dutch use of yew and box for topiary was introduced with William and Mary (Text Fig. 1).

PINE FAMILY: *Pináceae*

Usually monoecious trees and shrubs. Includes most of the cultivated conifers. Those below are perhaps the most frequently seen in Britain.

2. LAWSON'S CYPRESS, *Chamaecýparis Lawsoniána*. Spring.

A slender, pyramidal, evergreen tree, generally called *Cupréssus Lawsoniána*. One of the most frequently planted ornamental conifers. It has produced many varieties, one of which var. *Alumii*, a slow-growing, rather blue, upright tree is very popular in suburban gardens. Most forms are more drooping. The foliage is fern-like, the small scale leaves are shown enlarged (inset *b*). The male flowers are small, reddish-coloured. The cones (inset *a*) are at first green but turn brown. Introduced in 1845. A valuable timber tree but not grown as such in Britain (Text Fig. 2).

3. JUNIPER, *Juníperus commúnis, common*. Spring.

Usually found as an evergreen, rather prostrate, shrub, but sometimes a small tree. Flowers small and brownish. 'Berries' almost black and covered with 'bloom'; they yield an oil with diuretic properties, and are used in the flavouring of gin. Of downland. The Virginian juniper (*J. virginiána, Virginian*), known also as the red or pencil cedar, is a N. American tree found in cultivation. The timber (imported) has good weather- and insect-resisting properties, and has become popular for roofing, horticultural and agricultural buildings, etc. though long used for these purposes in its home.

4. COMMON LARCH, *Lárix decídua, decíduous*. Spring.

A tall, erect, deciduous tree. The male flowers yellow, female reddish-purple. The cone is shown (inset *a*). The branchlets are yellowish. Native of the mountains of C. and S. Europe, it was introduced in the seventeenth century, and has become one of our most valuable and widely planted conifers. Of recent years it has become affected by a canker, to which the Japanese larch (*L. leptolépis, with slender scales*) is resistant. It is rather similar in appearance, but is identified by the shorter cones (inset *b*) and the reddish branchlets. Introduced from Japan in 1861, it is now much used in forestry (Text Fig. 4).

5. SCOTS PINE, *Pínus sylvéstris, wild*. Spring.

An evergreen tree, the bark of the upper part of the stem having a reddish colour. The bluish-green leaves are in pairs, between 2 in. and 3 in. long, enclosed in a sheath at the base (inset *b*). Male flowers, yellow. Cone about 2½ in. long. An immature first season's cone is

C

shown (inset *a*). A valuable timber tree on poor, sandy soil. Still truly native in the north, but elsewhere planted and naturalized. The Corsican pine (*P. nígra, black,* var. *calábrica, from Calabria, South Italy*) is one of the commonest introduced pines. Brought from S. Europe in 1759, it is a tall evergreen tree with very rough pale⁄brown (never red) bark. The leaves, in pairs, are dark⁄green, and up to 7 in. long. Cones, silvery brown, about 3 in. long by 1¼ in. The Austrian pine

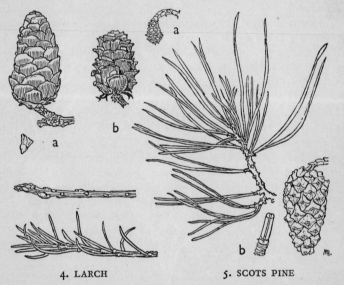

4. LARCH   5. SCOTS PINE

(*P. nígra,* var. *austríaca, Austrian*) is rather similar to the Corsican, but much more densely branched and leaved, with a spreading habit and gnarled appearance.

The common silver fir (*Ábies álba, white*) has glossy green leaves, about 1 in. long, closely arranged in two rows. It is a tall, pyramidal and symmetrical tree. Cones erect, 6 in. long by 2 in. Native of the mountains of C. and S. Europe, introduced in the seventeenth century.

The monkey⁄puzzle or Chile pine (*Araúco araucána, from the Arauco province of Chile*) has its branches arranged in tiers, from five to seven in a tier. Leaves dark⁄green, spiny, about 2 in. long and 1 in. wide, arranged closely in a spiral along the branch; they live for as much as fifteen years and then hang dead on the tree indefinitely. The big seeds

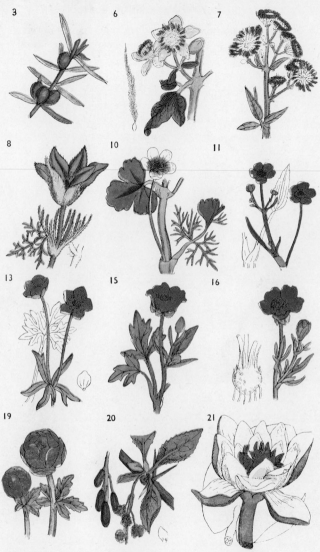

3. JUNIPER.
8. PASQUE FLOWER.
13. GOLDILOCKS.
19. GLOBE-FLOWER.

6. TRAVELLER'S JOY.
10. WATER CROW-
    FOOT.
15. CREEPING BUTTERCUP.
20. COMMON BAR-
    BERRY.

7. MEADOW RUE.
11. LESSER SPEAR-
    WORT.
16. BULBOUS BUTTER-
    CUP.
21. WHITE WATERLILY.

are used as food. Introduced in 1795 by A. Menzies, who sowed some of the seeds put on for dessert while on board ship.

The cedars, including the cedar of Lebanon (*Cédrus Libáni*), introduced from Asia Minor in the seventeenth century, with short tufted leaves and erect cylindrical cones 5 in. long by 2½ in., and the deodar (*C. Deodára*) introduced from the Himalayas in 1831, with short tufted leaves, erect egg-shaped cones 4 in. by 3 in., and drooping branchlets.

Common or Norway spruce (*Pícea Ábies*), the Christmas tree, provides the white deal imported from Norway. Densely branched, with small deep-green leaves in two rows. The branchlets are pale brown. Cone cylindrical, hanging, 5 in. long by 2 in. Introduced from C. or N. Europe in the sixteenth century. The Sitka spruce (*P. sitchénsis, of Sitka*) from western N. America has been much planted of recent years. It has yellowish branchlets, the leaves being larger than in the last and silvery on one side. Cone up to 4 in. long by 1 in. Both are important timber trees requiring a moist climate.

The wellingtonia (*Sequoía gigántea, gigantic*) is one of the largest, though not tallest, trees known. In its native California existing trees were probably growing in the time of Christ. A tall, narrow tree with small pointed leaves about ½ in. long. Cones 3 in. long by 2 in. The reddish-coloured bark is soft and fibrous. Introduced in 1853, it was extensively planted in parks and large gardens during last century.

The douglas fir (*Pseudotsúga Doúglasii*) or Oregon douglas, is a tall tree with a pointed crown. Leaves narrow, 1 in. long, arranged spirally. Bark greyish. Cones hanging, 2 in. long by 1 in., bearing remarkable three-pronged projecting bracts. A timber tree introduced from western N. America in 1827.

II. Angiosperms

Plants with the seeds enclosed by a fruit, or more accurately, by that part of the fruit which was formerly the ovary, or *pericarp*.

IIa. Dicotyledons

Plants with two lobes, or seed-leaves, present in the seed. When perennial the stems have pith in the centre surrounded by concentric rings of woody tissue, with bark on the outside. Usually, the leaves are veined in a net-like system, and the parts of the flowers are in fours, fives, or eights.

BUTTERCUP FAMILY: *Ranunculáceae*

A family for the most part consisting of herbaceous perennials distributed in the north temperate regions, becoming mountain plants in the tropics.

Leaves usually alternate when on the stems, except in *Clématis* when they are opposite. Sepals usually five. Petals usually five, often insignificant and sometimes missing altogether; in such cases the sepals often are petal-like. Stamens numerous. Fruit consists of several achenes, a cluster of pods, or sometimes a berry.

The following are some of the many cultivated kinds: winter aconite (*Eránthis hyemális, of winter*) from Italy; devil-in-the-bush (*Nigélla damascéna, Damascene*) from S. Europe; monk's-hood (*Aconítum*) from C. Europe; numerous paeonies (*Paeónia*) from S. Europe and China; the columbines (*Aquilégia*), of which one kind is a native but which when found is often escaped from cultivation; and the larkspurs (*Delphínium*)—the big modern herbaceous kinds being hybrids of mixed and cosmopolitan parentage, though many species are European. The Christmas rose (*Hellebórus niger, black*) and the Lenten rose (*H. orientális, from the East*) which come from C. and S. Europe and have been long grown in gardens, have British relatives which are occasionally found, usually on chalk soils. They are the stinking hellebore or setterwort (*H. foétidus, stinking*) and the bear's-foot or green hellebore (*H. víridis, green*). Both are easily distinguished by their greenish-yellow flowers (the petal-like sepals being the most conspicuous part), opening from February to April. Both have handsome leaves divided into five or six leaflets; the green hellebore is the smaller plant of the two, about 1 ft. high. All are poisonous, and once much used medicinally.

Many of this family have a highly poisonous acrid juice for their protection, often containing anemonol, which affects the nervous system, or poisonous alkaloids. Several yield valuable drugs, especially *Aconitum*, which is, however, very poisonous.

6. TRAVELLER'S JOY, OLD MAN'S BEARD, *Clématis Vitálba*. Late summer.

A perennial climber. Leaves opposite and compound, usually with five leaflets. The leaf-stalks are used as tendrils. The flowers are scented, without petals but with showy sepals. The numerous styles develop into a feathery mass, the 'old man's beard.' Of hedgerows, particularly on chalk soils in C. and S. Britain. Many clematis are grown in gardens, mostly showy hybrids, with parents introduced from S. Europe, China, Japan, and N. America. None have petals.

7. MEADOW RUE, *Thalíctrum flávum, yellow*. Summer.

Perennial, with a creeping yellow rootstock and stout, furrowed stem up to 3 ft. high and large compound leaves. Sepals, four, stamens prominent, yellow. Of moist meadows and ditches, uncommon in the N. *T. aquilegifólium, aquilegia-leaved*, from Europe and W. Asia, is one of several introduced kinds grown in gardens. Fruit a number of achenes. Name from Greek *thallein*, to bloom, from the numerous flowers.

8. PASQUE FLOWER, *Anemóne Pulsatílla*. Spring.

Perennial, about 8 in. high. Flowers before the leaves appear (reputedly at Eastertide, hence the name). Six petal-like sepals serve the purpose of petals; the flower-stalk bears a whorl of three leaf-like bracts. Leaves finely divided, and, like the flower, hairy. The fruit has feathery tails like a clematis. The leaves supplied the old drug pulsatilla. Of chalk and limestone pastures in England only.

9. WOOD ANEMONE, WINDFLOWER, *Anemóne nemorósa, of woods*. Early to late spring.

Perennial, about 8 in. high, with a creeping black rootstock. The flower has about six white or slightly pink-tinted petal-like sepals on a stem which bears a whorl of three leaf-like bracts. This plant, rather variable in flower, is frequent in woody places in Britain, throughout Europe, in N.-W. Asia and N. America (Text Fig. 9). Besides selected forms of *A. nemorosa* many kinds of this large and widespread genus are cultivated, particularly the gay and many-coloured florist's forms of the crown or poppy anemone (*A. coronária, crown*) flowering in early spring and introduced from S. Europe in the sixteenth century, and the tall Japanese anemone (*A. japónica, Japanese*) brought from China during the last century, which flowers in the late summer. The name windflower (Greek, *anemos,* wind) has been explained in several ways, none very definite.

10. WATER CROWFOOT, *Ranúnculus aquátilis, of water*. Early summer.

An aquatic perennial, variable in form, but the leaves usually very finely cut when submerged, much less so when above or out of water.

The flowers are held on straight stalks above the water. Found floating in still water or running along and rooting from the stem in mud.

11. LESSER SPEARWORT, *Ranúnculus Flámmula*.   Spring to autumn.

Perennial or annual, much branched, with stems which often lie along the ground and root before they ascend to 1 ft. or so high. Leaves undivided, lower much rounder than the upper.   Of muddy

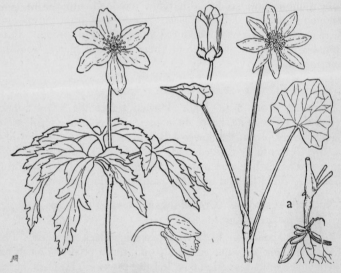

9. WOOD ANEMONE   12. LESSER CELANDINE

and damp situations.   The greater spearwort (*R. Língua*) is less common, and quite twice the size.

12. LESSER CELANDINE, PILEWORT, *Ranúnculus Ficaria*.   Early
     spring.

Perennial, the rootstock emitting tubers (see inset).   The leaves very variable in shape, from ivy to heartshaped.   Stems about 6 in. high. Flowers bright yellow, opening in mild weather from February onwards.   Of banks, hedgerows, and light woodland (Text Fig. 12).

13. GOLDILOCKS, WOOD CROWFOOT, *Ranúnculus auricomus, with
     golden hairs*.   Spring.

An erect perennial, hairless or nearly so, about 1 ft. high, with a branching stem. Lower leaves on long stalks. Of open woods and copses in England, but less common in Ireland and Scotland. The flowers are sometimes without, or with deformed, petals.

14. BUTTERCUP, CROWFOOT, *Ranúnculus ácris, bitter.* Summer to autumn.

An erect perennial covered with soft hairs, the lower leaves intri-cately divided, nearly all being stalked. Varying in size according to

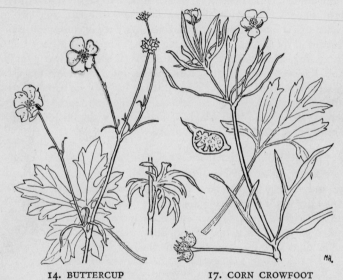

14. BUTTERCUP   17. CORN CROWFOOT

situation, from a few inches to 3 ft. Flowers golden-yellow. Abun-dant in cultivated and waste places, particularly grassland (Text Fig. 14). A double form grown in gardens is the original 'bachelor's buttons.'

15. CREEPING BUTTERCUP or CROWFOOT, *Ranúnculus répens, creeping.* Summer to autumn.

Perennial, rather similar to the above but usually not so tall. Readily distinguished by the numerous runners it sends out, which root freely and form new plants—making it a most troublesome weed to eradicate —and the stalked terminal leaf-segment. Abundant in similar situations to the last.

16. BULBOUS BUTTERCUP or CROWFOOT, *Ranúnculus bulbósus, bulbous.* Early summer.

Perennial similar to the above, but smaller in all its parts and more hairy. Easily identified by the bulbous swelling at the base of the stems and reflexed sepals. Does not creep. Of similar situations.

17. CORN CROWFOOT or BUTTERCUP, *Ranúnculus arvénsis, of culti-vated fields.* Summer.

An annual, erect, branching, from ¾ ft. to 2 ft. high. Leaves pale-green, smooth. Flowers small, pale yellow, and the seeds, contained in a spiny carpel (inset), ripen with the corn. A weed of cultivation, more frequent in the S. than N. (Text Fig. 17). The name is from Latin *rana,* a frog, alluding to the situation of several species in wet ground. Most *Ranunculus* contain an irritant poison, but are so bitter that they are seldom touched by stock; when dried in hay they are harmless. In gardens, florist's forms of *R. asiáticus, Asiatic,* introduced from the Levant, are grown. Fair Maids of France is the double form of the continental *R. aconitifólium, aconite-leaved.*

18. MARSH MARIGOLD, KING-CUP, *Cáltha palústris, of marshes.* Spring.

Perennial, rather variable, about 1 ft. high, the stems usually spread-ing and rooting as they go. About five petal-like sepals form the showy part of the golden-coloured flower. Of marshes, wet meadows, and watersides. It is popular and bears many local names, such as luckan gowan in the north. Poisonous. Name from Greek *kalathos,* a cup, alluding to the shape of the flower (Text Fig. 18).

19. GLOBE-FLOWER, *Tróllius europaéus, European.* Summer.

Perennial, forming large tufts, with a thick rootstock. Stems often spreading and rooting before they ascend to about 1 ft. high. The flower has about twelve showy sepals curved into the shape of a cup, enclosing a similar number of insignificant petals. Of moist places in the Welsh and northern mountains. Name from Latin *trulleus,* a bowl, from the flower-shape. The finer forms, and European and Asiatic kinds, are grown in gardens.

BARBERRY FAMILY: *Berberidáceae*

A cosmopolitan family of herbs and shrubs, best known in Britain by the many introduced barberries. Other garden representatives are the herbaceous *Epimédiums*, from Europe and Asia, and the Indian *Podophýllum*, from which a drug is produced.

20. COMMON BARBERRY, *Bérberis vulgáris, common*. Spring to early summer.

A deciduous shrub with arching branches about 8 ft. high, or taller. Armed with three-lobed spines which are in reality modified leaves. Like most other barberries, it has yellow wood and roots, and small yellow flowers having six petals with from six to nine sepals. The fruit is a red berry, about ½ in. long, very acid, but once preserved in sugar. The wheat rust fungus spends a period of its life on the common barberry; it should, therefore, not be planted near wheat-fields. Of the numerous introduced barberries and their close allies the mahonias, *Mahónia Aquifólium* from western N. America is the commonest, being extensively planted as an undergrowth in plantations. It is a low, suckering shrub with leaves consisting of several large dark green leaflets, spiny at the tips, colouring in winter. The yellow flowers, in erect racemes, open in spring, and are followed by numerous dark-purple, bloom-covered berries. *B. stenophýlla, narrow-leaved*, is a dense bush with red stems, often 10 ft. high, bearing narrow evergreen leaves about 1 in. long. It is a hybrid of British origin. Numerous smaller deciduous barberries introduced from Asia during the present century are very popular.

WATERLILY FAMILY: *Nymphaeáceae*

A rather variable family of tropical and temperate water plants, usually with submerged roots, rounded leaves floating on or above the surface, and fleshy fruits.

It includes the gigantic *Victória régia, royal*, from tropical America, and the gaily coloured *Nelúmbium speciósum, showy*, reputed to be the lotus of Egypt, though native of tropical Asia.

21. WHITE WATERLILY, *Nymphaéa álba, white*. Summer.

Perennial, the heart-shaped leaves being about 8 in. diameter. Flowers scentless, floating on the water, the sepals appearing to be outer petals. Fruit submerged, seeds liberated when the pulpy cover rots. Of still and slow-running water. Dedicated by the Greeks to the water-nymphs. Hybridization with this and foreign species has produced the many beautiful kinds seen in greenhouses.

22. YELLOW WATERLILY, BRANDY-BOTTLE, *Núphar lúteum, golden-yellow*. Summer.

Perennial with leaves similar to the above. The flowers, with a sickly scent, are held an inch or two above the water. The sepals are yellow and showy, the petals insignificant. The large green fruits are

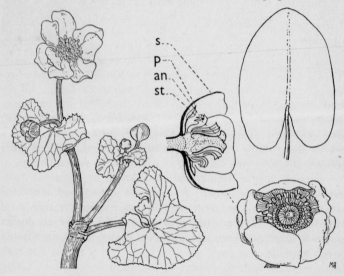

18. MARSH MARIGOLD   22. YELLOW WATERLILY

on the surface, liberating the seeds when they rot; they are the shape of a flagon, or brandy-bottle (Text Fig. 22).

POPPY FAMILY: *Papaveráceae*

A family, mostly herbaceous, growing principally in north temperate regions, and containing *latex*.[1]

In British species, the leaves are alternate, divided, and without stipules. The flower has two sepals which fall when it opens, and four petals, crumpled, not folded, in the bud. Stamens numerous, stigma a rayed disk. Fruit a pod or capsule. The plants usually hairy.

[1] A white or yellow milky fluid contained in special vessels.

23. FIELD POPPY, *Papáver Rhoéas.* Summer.

A hairy annual between 1 ft. and 2 ft. high. Of waste and cultivated land (where it is a troublesome weed), rather commoner in the S. than N. There are several rather similar species. All are strongly narcotic and poisonous, but their unpleasant smell and taste usually prevents stock from eating them. The tall opium poppy (*P. somniferum, sleep-bearing*) from S. Europe has long been cultivated in gardens in its showy and double forms, and is found naturalized. Opium is the dried latex exuded by the seed-heads when they are cut. An oil is pressed from poppy seeds.

24. WELSH POPPY, *Meconópsis cámbrica, Welsh.* Summer.

Perennial, about 1 ft. high. Flowers pale yellow on slender stems. Leaves pale-green and hairy. Of shady and rocky woods in Wales, Ireland, and western England. Name from Greek *mekon,* poppy; *opsis,* resemblance (Text Fig. 24).

25. GREATER CELANDINE, *Chelidónium május, great.* Summer.

Perennial with slender erect branching stems up to 2 ft. high. Of roadsides and waste places, particularly near buildings. Contains an acrid poisonous juice once used as an eye medicine and for burning warts. No relative of lesser celandine (No. 12)—it is said that both were connected with the return of the swallow, called in Greek *chelidon.*

26. HORNED POPPY, *Glaúcium flávum, yellow.* Summer.

An annual or biennial of strong spreading growth, about 2 ft. high, of a blue-green colour. Of sea-shores, uncommon in the north. The 'horn' is the long ovary.

FUMITORY FAMILY: *Fumariáceae*

Very similar to, and often included with, the poppy family, but distinguished by the irregular petals, one being spurred, and the absence of latex. Fruit, a pod or nutlet.

The lyre-flowers, or (incorrectly) dielytras, of gardens and greenhouses, species of *Dícentra* from Asia and N. America, belong to this family.

27. COMMON FUMITORY, *Fumária officinális*,[1] *of use to man*. Summer to autumn.

An annual of delicate trailing growth with pale‑green leaves. Of waste places and spread as a weed of cultivation over many parts of the world. Once of great repute medicinally. There are several similar species. One, *F. capreolata, having tendrils*, being a climber. Name from Latin *fumus*, smoke, alluding to its smoke‑like appearance, or perhaps its smell.

28. CLIMBING CORYDALIS, *Corydális claviculáta, with forked tendrils*. Summer.

An annual, having a mass of intricate stems, climbing by means of the forked tendrils, which are extensions of the leaf‑stalk. Of hedgerows and thickets. Yellow corydalis (*C. lútea, yellow*) with larger flowers than the above, pale yellow, is a S. European plant naturalized on old buildings and walls. Name from Greek *korydalis*, a crested lark, from the appearance of its flowers.

WALLFLOWER OR CRUCIFER FAMILY: *Cruciferae*

A large family, chiefly north temperate, with some 19,000 species, mostly herbs.

Distinguished by the cross‑shaped flower (page 8 and Plate II), which is generally white, yellow, or purple. Fruit a pod, usually divided into two by a thin longitudinal partition.

Many genera yield important foodstuffs (see below), while numerous S. European kinds have been grown in gardens for centuries, and are now sometimes naturalized. Such are stocks (*Matthióla*), wall‑flower (*Cheiránthus*), rockcress (*Árabis*), alison (*Alýssum*), and candy‑tuft (*Ibéris*). Honesty (*Lunária*) and *Aubrétia* are also introduced crucifers. Woad (*Isátis tinctória, used for dyeing*), the pigment used by the early Britons, is sometimes found in Britain. *Cruciferae*, from the Latin, means *cross‑bearers*.

29. WINTER CRESS, YELLOW ROCKET, *Barbaréa vulgáris, common*. Spring to summer.

A perennial with deeply furrowed stems and dark‑green shiny leaves

---

[1] Literally, *of the shop*, i.e. sold for man's use.

lasting over winter. Flower stem 1 ft. to 2 ft. Of moist hedgerows and waste places. Once used as a salad. Dedicated to St Barbara.

30. COMMON WATERCRESS, *Nastúrtium officinále, of use to man.* Summer.

An aquatic perennial, the hollow stem rooting as it runs in the mud. From 6 in. to 9 in. high. Well known as a salad. The nasturtium

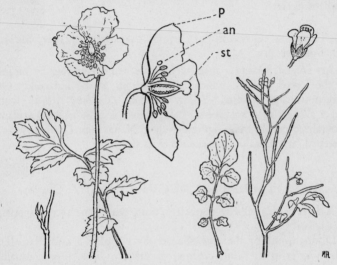

24. WELSH POPPY   32. HAIRY BITTERCRESS

of flower gardens is no relative; it is a S. American *Tropaeólum* related to the geranium family.

31. LADY's-SMOCK, CUCKOO-FLOWER, MILKMAIDS, *Cardamine praténsis, of meadows.* Spring to early summer.

An erect perennial, about 1 ft. high. The radical leaves lying on wet ground root at each leaflet, forming a new plant at each axil. Of damp meadows and stream-sides.

32. HAIRY BITTERCRESS, *Cardamine hirsúta, hairy.* Spring to late summer.

An annual from an inch or so to 1 ft. high with scattered hairs.

Leaves dark-green, variable in size and shape, the radical ones usually in a rosette. Flowers white, small. Of damp and shady places in waste and cultivated ground (Text Fig. 32).

33. HEDGE MUSTARD, *Sisýmbrium officinále, of use to man.* Summer.

An erect annual, with stiff horizontal branches, about 1 ft. high. Leaves deeply cut or lobed, downy. Of waste places and waysides.

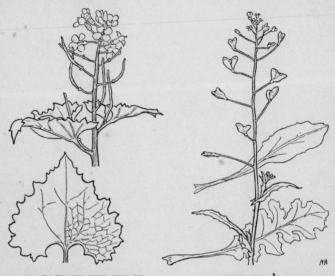

34. JACK-BY-THE-HEDGE   39. SHEPHERD'S PURSE

34. JACK - BY - THE -HEDGE, GARLIC - MUSTARD, SAUCE - ALONE, *Alliária officinális, of use to man.* Spring to early summer.

Annual or biennial of erect growth, up to 3 ft. high. Flowers small, white. Smells of garlic when crushed. Of hedgerows and shady places. Name from Latin *allium*, garlic (Text Fig. 34).

35. FIELD CABBAGE, NAVEW, *Brássica campéstris, of the plains.* Spring to summer.

An annual, stems up to 2 ft. high. Lower leaves stalked, divided, with a terminal lobe, bluish-green and hairy; upper, stem-clasping. Sepals erect. A frequent weed of cultivation. Cultivated forms allied to this are the turnip (*B. Rápa*), rape or colza (*B. Nápa*), and

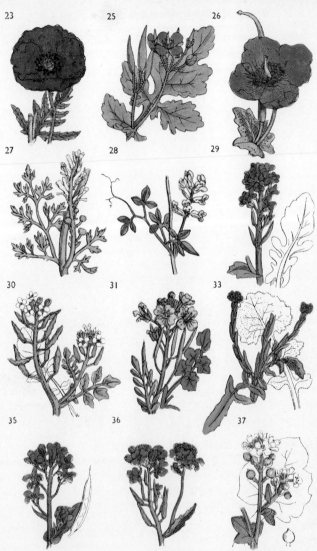

23. FIELD POPPY.
27. COMMON FUMITORY.
30. COMMON WATER-
        CRESS.
35. FIELD CABBAGE.

25. CELANDINE.
28. CLIMBING CORY-
        DALYIS.
31. LADY'S-SMOCK.
36. CHARLOCK.

26. HORNED POPPY.
29. WINTER CRESS.
33. HEDGE MUSTARD.
37. SCURVY-GRASS.

swede (*B. Rutabága*). The wild cabbage (*B. olerácea, edible*) is a sea-coast plant found locally in Britain, and is the parent of the garden cabbage, cauliflower, broccoli, kale, and savoy.

36. CHARLOCK, WILD MUSTARD, *Brássica Sinápis*. Summer.

A hairy annual, lower leaves lyre-shaped with roughly toothed edges; upper, not stem-clasping. Sepals spreading. Stems from 1 ft. to 2 ft. high. A weed of cultivation, probably originating in S. Europe. Oil of mustard in the seeds makes them poisonous in quantity.

37. SCURVY-GRASS, *Cochleária officinális, of use to man*. Summer.

A smooth and rather fleshy annual or biennial, from 4 in. to 1 ft. high. Of shores and along rivers. Several forms are differentiated. Once used as a remedy for scurvy. The horse-radish is *C. Armorácia* from S.-E. Europe. Name from Latin *cochlear*, a spoon, from the leaf-shape.

38. COMMON WHITLOW-GRASS, *Drába vérna, spring*. Early spring to early summer.

An annual, lasting only a few weeks, from 3 in. to 6 in. high. Leaves in a rosette. Of walls and banks. Name from Greek *drabe*, acrid.

39. SHEPHERD'S-PURSE, *Capsélla Búrsa-pastóris*. Most of year.

An annual, very variable in size and form, from an inch or two to over 1 ft. Flowers white, minute, and without nectar or scent. A weed of cultivated and waste places. Name from Latin *capsula*, a small box (Text Fig. 39).

40. PEPPERWORT, *Lepídium campéstre, of the plain*. Summer.

An annual or biennial about 1 ft. high, rather similar to the above, covered with minute downy hairs. Of dry waste places and fields. Garden cress is *L. satívum, cultivated*, from Asia. Name from Greek *lepidion*, a scale, from the scaly pods.

41. WART-CRESS, SWINE-CRESS, *Coronópus Ruélli*. Summer to autumn.

A small pale-green annual, with stems which at first form a tuft, but after flowering spread along the ground. Of fields and waste places, particularly in the south. Name from Greek *korone*, crow, and *pous*, foot, referring to the leaves.

42. SEA ROCKET, *Cakíle marítima, of the sea.* Summer to autumn.

A straggling branching annual, about ¾ ft. high, with few, fleshy, divided leaves, covered with a 'bloom.' Of sandy coasts and salt-marshes.

43. SEA-KALE, *Crámbe marítima, of the sea.* Early summer.

A perennial with branched stems up to 2 ft. high. Leaves handsome, bluish in colour, fleshy, lobed, and waved at the edges. Of sea-coasts, not common. Cultivated as a vegetable.

44. WILD RADISH, JOINTED CHARLOCK, *Ráphanus Raphanístrum.* Summer onwards.

Usually a branching annual up to 2 ft. high, resembling charlock (No. 36), from which it is distinguished by its upright, not spreading, sepals and veined, often white, petals. Pods often jointed. A weed of cultivation. The origin of the cultivated form is obscure.

MIGNONETTE FAMILY: *Resedáceae*

A small family of herbs, uncommon in Britain. The sweet-scented Egyptian *Reséda odoráta, scented* has long been cultivated. Dyer's rocket or weld (*R. lúteola, yellowish*) was grown for its yellow juice, which made a dye. Wild mignonette (*R. lútea, yellow*) has unscented yellow flowers on long stems and deeply cut leaves. Both grow in waste places.

ROCK-ROSE FAMILY: *Cistáceae*

Herbs or shrubs, usually of dry, sunny places, particularly in the Mediterranean regions, and on chalky or sandy soils.

Leaves usually simple and opposite. Flowers mostly with five petals. Sepals five, the two outer being smaller, or sometimes three only. Fruit a capsule. Introduced S. European *Cistus* have long been cultivated.

45. SUN-ROSE, *Heliánthemum Chamaecístus.* Summer.

A low trailing shrub. The narrow leaves are green above and grey, with short hairs, below. Much of the plant dies back in winter, the rest is evergreen. Flower with three large and two very small sepals. Of chalk downs, stony banks, and dry pastures. Many varieties and also hybrids, as well as foreign species, are grown in gardens. Name

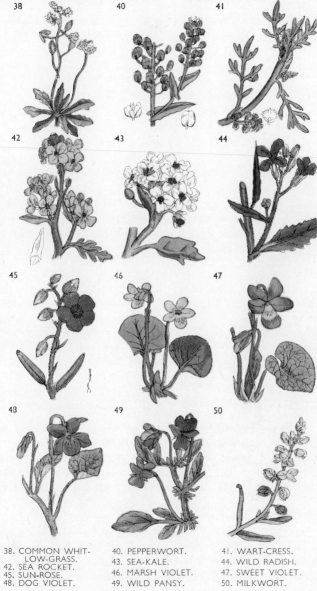

38. COMMON WHIT-
       LOW-GRASS.
42. SEA ROCKET.
45. SUN-ROSE.
48. DOG VIOLET.

40. PEPPERWORT.
43. SEA-KALE.
46. MARSH VIOLET.
49. WILD PANSY.

41. WART-CRESS.
44. WILD RADISH.
47. SWEET VIOLET.
50. MILKWORT.

from Greek *helios*, sun, and *anthos*, flower. Often called rock-rose, which should be restricted to *Cistus*.

VIOLET FAMILY: *Violáceae*

The herbaceous *Viola* is the only British genus of this cosmopolitan family, which includes trees and shrubs. The viola, with its five petals, the lowest spurred, is so well known that the genus is easily recognized. Fruit a capsule. It is spread widely over the world, and numerous forms are well known in gardens, alpine species being popular in rock-gardens. The florist's violas and pansies are hybrids of mixed origin. All here described are perennial.

Certain species produce most of their seed from insignificant flowers, little more than unopened buds containing the essential organs for reproduction, formed generally when the showy flowers are faded.

46. MARSH VIOLET, *Viola palústris, of marshes*. Spring to early summer.

A small plant with scentless flowers found in marshy ground. Abundant in Scotland.

47. SWEET VIOLET, *Viola odoráta, scented*. Spring; petal-less flowers throughout the summer.

Known by its scent, and its creeping, rooting, running stems. Flowers vary to white. Of hedgerows, field-sides, banks and woodland. Common locally, not found in Ireland. Often naturalized.

48. DOG VIOLET, *Viola canína, dog*. Spring to early summer; petal-less flowers later.

Not unlike the above in appearance, but without scent. It is the commonest kind, and several distinct species are separated, as it is very variable.

49. WILD PANSY, HEARTSEASE, *Viola trícolor, three-coloured*. Spring to autumn.

Distinguished by its two upper petals which are upstanding and do not lean forward as in the other species, and its flowers of white, yellow, or purple, or a mixture of these. No petal-less flowers are produced. Of waste ground, banks, etc. and as a weed of cultivation.

D

MILKWORT FAMILY: *Polygaláceae*

Represented in Europe by *Polygala* alone.

50. MILKWORT, *Polýgala vulgáris, common.* Summer.

A small much-branched perennial, from 2 in. to 6 in. high, forming a tuft, with alternate lance-shaped leaves. Flowers vary from pink to blue, or sometimes white, in a terminal raceme. Fruit a capsule. Of dry heaths, hedgerows, and pastures. Name from Greek *polus*, much, and *galus*, milk, from its reputed effect on milk production.

PINK FAMILY: *Caryophylláceae*

A large family of herbs (and a few undershrubs) with some thirteen thousand species distributed over the world.

Generally distinguishable by their narrow, entire leaves, growing in pairs, opposite; the rounded stems jointed and swollen at the base of each pair. Flowers with four or five petals and sepals, the sepals often joined in a long tube. Fruit a capsule.

Several kinds of *Gypsóphila* from S. Europe and Asia are well known in gardens. The soapworts (*Saponária*) are also cultivated; *S. officinális, of use to man,* is found in Britain, though usually naturalized.

51. MAIDEN PINK, *Diánthus deltoídes, delta-like.* Summer.

A low, spreading, tufted perennial with short grass-like leaves. Stems up to 1 ft. high. Flowers scentless, usually pink, and often marked with spots shaped like the Greek *Δ*, hence the name. Of dry banks and pastures (Text Fig. 51). From C. and S. Europe come *D. barbátus, bearded,* the origin of the sweet-william, and *D. Caryophýllus* (said to have been brought with the Normans), an important ancestor of the carnation and clove pink. The Cheddar pink (*D. caésius, bluish-grey*), with fragrant rose-coloured flowers, is found wild in Britain only on the limestone Cheddar rocks. Name means *Jove's flower*.

52. MOSS CAMPION, DWARF CATCHFLY, *Siléne acaúlis, stemless.* Summer.

A perennial of moss-like, tufted growth, found on mountains, particularly in Scotland. Flowers sometimes white.

53. Bladder-campion, Whitebottle, *Siléne Cucúbalus.* Summer to early autumn.

A loosely branched perennial, flower-stems up to 1 ft. high, with white flowers. Of banks, waysides, waste places, and fields (Text Fig. 53). The sea-campion (*S. marítima, of the sea*) found on coasts

51. MAIDEN PINK   53. BLADDER-CAMPION

has fewer and larger flowers and shorter stems. Name from Greek *sialon*, saliva, from the stickiness of some kinds.

54. Red Campion, *Lýchnis dioíca, dioecious.* Spring onwards.

This and the white campion (*L. álba, white*) illustrated with it, are rather similar. Both are loosely branched biennials, with hairy and rather sticky leaves. Stems from 1 ft. to 2 ft. high. Male and female flowers usually distinct. In *L. dioica* they are secntless and open by day, in *L. alba* slightly scented and open at night, being fertilized by moths. Both are of hedgerows, fields, and waste places.

55. Corn-cockle, *Lýchnis Githágo.* Summer to autumn.

A tall annual up to 5 ft. high, hairy, with long narrow leaves.

Flowers on long leafless stalks, the calyx with odd leafy teeth projecting beyond the petals. A weed of cultivation in cornfields, perhaps not native.

56. RAGGED ROBIN, *Lýchnis Flos-cúculi*. Spring to summer.

A perennial of erect growth, up to 2 ft. high. Leaves rather few, lance-shaped. The whole plant is sticky and reddish-coloured. The petals are deeply cut into four segments giving a ragged appearance. Sometimes called cuckoo-flower from its Latin specific name, but this really belongs only to No. 31. Of moist meadows and ditches. Name from Greek *luchnos*, a torch, alluding to the flame-colour of some species.

57. COMMON PEARLWORT, *Sagína procúmbens, trailing*. Spring to autumn.

A small grassy plant growing in tufts, an inch or two high. Very common in heaths and sandy soils, and a troublesome weed in gardens. Very variable in size. Knotted pearlwort (*S. nodósa, knotted*) has larger flowers carried on stems a little taller than in the last; of moist places.

58. SEA SANDWORT, SEA PURSLANE, *Arenária peploídes, Peplis-like*. Early summer.

A dark-green creeping perennial, forming mats. Leaves many and rather fleshy. Flowers few and insignificant, in leafy terminal cymes, producing large, round seed-vessels. Of the sea-shore.

59. THYME-LEAVED SANDWORT, *Arenária serpyllifólia, thyme-leaved*. Summer.

A small, slender, branching annual, from 2 in. to 4 in. high, with small, pointed leaves. Of dry, stony places and walls.

60. THREE-NERVED OR PLANTAIN-LEAVED SANDWORT, *Arenária trinérvia, three-nerved*. Spring to early summer.

A weak, spreading annual, with stems up to 1 ft. long. Not unlike chickweed, but with undivided petals (divided into two in chickweed). Leaves with three marked veins or nerves. Of moist woods and shady places. Name from Latin *arena*, sand, most kinds thriving in sandy soils.

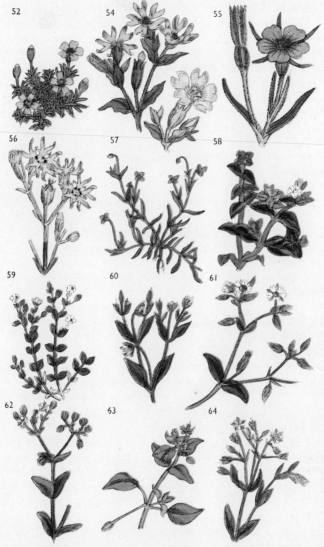

52. MOSS CAMPION.
56. RAGGED ROBIN.
59. THYME-LEAVED
    SANDWORT.
62. LITTLE MOUSE-EAR
    CHICKWEED.

54. RED CAMPION.
57. COMMON PEARL-
    WORT.
60. THREE-NERVED
    SANDWORT.
63. CHICKWEED.

55. CORN-COCKLE.
58. SEA SANDWORT.
61. MOUSE-EAR
    CHICKWEED.
64. BOG STITCH-
    WORT.

61. MOUSE-EAR CHICKWEED, *Cerástium viscósum, sticky.* Spring to autumn.

An annual, branching at the base, downy and sticky. Variable in height, sometimes over 1 ft. Very variable, and a number of closely allied forms are separated as species. Of many situations, wet or dry, but particularly in waste and cultivated land; widely spread over the world.

62. LITTLE MOUSE-EAR CHICKWEED, *Cerástium semidecándrum, with five stamens.* Spring.

A small, slender annual with soft, hairy leaves. One of the commonest plants on old walls and in dry, stony places. *C. vulgátum, well-known,* is a lusher plant common in moist places. *Mouse-ear* refers to the silky leaves like a mouse's ear. *Cerastium* is from Greek *keras,* horn, alluding to the shape of the capsule.

63. CHICKWEED, *Stellária média, intermediate.* Most of the year.

An annual with weak trailing stems bearing a single line of hairs which changes sides when a pair of leaves is reached. In many situations, particularly as a weed of cultivation. As such, it has been carried to most temperate parts of the world.

64. BOG STITCHWORT, *Stellária uliginósa, of marshes.* Spring to summer.

Annual, with weak, slender stems about 6 in. long, or less in dry ground. Petals shorter than the calyx. Found along ditches and in damp places.

65. LESSER STITCHWORT, *Stellária gramínea, grassy.* Summer.

A perennial with thin four-sided stems, reaching about 1 ft. Leaves longer and narrower than the last. Flowers white. Very common in dry fields and hedgerows (Text Fig. 65).

66. GREATER STITCHWORT, *Stellária Holóstea.* Spring to early summer.

Perennial, similar to the last in general appearance, but larger, the stems being four-sided and usually leaning on neighbouring plants for support; they are brittle. Flowers large. Of hedgerows. Name from Latin *stella,* star, from the flower-shape.

67. SANDSPURREY, *Spergulária rúbra, red.* Summer.

Annual or biennial, with many reddish stems branching from the root and lying flat along the ground, bearing tufts of narrow leaves at the ends. Flowers rather variable in size and colour, sometimes almost white. Of heaths and gravelly soils. There are several allied species, all sea-shore plants, very similar but with more fleshy leaves.

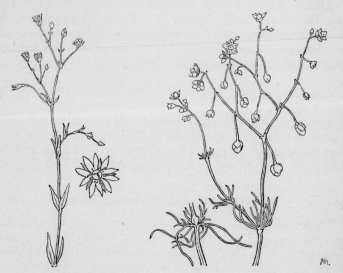

65. LESSER STITCHWORT   **68. CORN SPURREY**

68. CORN SPURREY, *Spérgula arvénsis, of cultivated fields.* Summer.

Annual, branching at the base into several fairly upright stems, up to 1 ft. high. Leaves almost round, growing in opposite clusters of six or eight together. Flowers white, the flower-stalks turning down when they fade. Of cultivated and waste places (Text Fig. 68). Name from Latin *spargo*, I scatter, referring to the abundant seed the plants spread about them.

PURSLANE FAMILY: *Portulacáceae*

A family, usually fleshy-leaved herbs, particularly associated with N. and S. America.

Often annuals, leaves usually succulent and entire, and generally opposite. Sepals two. Petals five. Fruit a capsule.

Several members are cultivated, particularly in greenhouses. The old herb purslane is *Portuláca olerácea, edible.* Its origin is doubtful.

69. CLAYTONIA, *Claytónia sibírica, Siberian.* Summer.

Annual, about 1 ft. high. Flowers pink or purplish (Text Fig. 69). Introduced from N. America, it is often found freely naturalized around shrubberies, as is *C. perfóliata, perfoliate,* which is smaller, with white flowers, the stem surrounded by the base of the leaf or *perfoliate.* Named after J. Clayton, a botanist (1693–1773).

70. BLINKS, WATER CHICKWEED, *Móntia fontána, of springs.* Spring to summer.

A small annual, forming dense green tufts an inch or two high. Found on the edges of springs and in damp places where the water does not stagnate. A plant whose remarkably wide range includes Europe, N. Asia, N. and S. America, Australia, and New Zealand.

TAMARISK FAMILY: *Tamaricáceae*

The common tamarisk (*Támarix gállica, French*) is a shrub which has been widely planted on our south coasts, and often appears to be wild. From 5 ft. to 10 ft. high, it has slender, feathery branches, with spikes of very small white or pink flowers in early summer. Some authorities claim one form as English. Named after the R. Tambre in Spain.

ST JOHN'S WORT FAMILY: *Guttiferae*

Represented in Britain by the genus *Hypéricum* alone, which here consists of herbs and semi-shrubs. All have yellow flowers with five petals and five sepals. Fruit a capsule. The leaves often show glands (inset, Text Fig. 73) of two kinds, one appearing as pellucid dots, the other as black marks, sometimes seen on the flower also.

Several kinds, mostly shrubs, have been introduced to gardens from S. Europe, America, Asia, the Canary and Azores Islands. All have the typical yellow flower. The Rose of Sharon (*H. calycínum, with a cup*) or Aaron's beard, a low bush with large bright yellow flowers in late summer, about 3 in. across, was brought from the Orient in the seventeenth century and has become naturalized.

71. COMMON ST JOHN'S WORT, *Hypéricum perforátum, pierced* (the leaves). Summer to autumn.

Perennial, making runners, with upright stems about a foot high which carry the flowers in a showy terminal corymb. The leaves, marked with numerous clear dots, are about ½ in. long, without stalks. Of copses and hedgerows.

69. CLAYTONIA   73. TRAILING ST JOHN'S WORT

72. SQUARE-STALKED ST JOHN'S WORT, *Hypéricum quadrángulum, four-angled.* Summer.

Rather similar to the above, but stem has four very marked angles, and the leaves are larger. Of moist places.

73. TRAILING ST JOHN'S WORT, *Hypéricum humifúsum, spreading on the ground.* Summer to autumn.

Much smaller than any of the above, with a trailing, prostrate growth. Flowers small and yellow (Text Fig. 73).

Other natives are tutsan (*H. Androsaémum*), somewhat shrubby, about 2 ft. high, with leaves up to 2 in. long, and rather few flowers, ¾ in. across, found in open woods of W. England; slender St John's wort (*H. púlchrum, beautiful*), of slender, upright growth, between 1 ft.

and 2 ft. high, with small flowers in a panicle, of dry woods and heaths; and hairy St John's wort (*H. hirsútum, hairy*), rather similar to the last but taller, with longer leaves, hairy stems, and found in woods and thickets.

FLAX FAMILY: *Lináceae*

A cosmopolitan family including herbs, shrubs, and trees.

In Britain, herbs with usually undivided, alternate leaves. The flower-parts are usually in fives. Fruit a capsule.

All-seed or flax-seed (*Radíola linioídes, flax-like*) is a minute annual found locally on sandy heaths. It is an inch or so high, and repeatedly branched, bearing a great many small white flowers having their parts in fours, not fives.

74. PURGING FLAX, *Línum cathárticum, purgative.* Summer.

A slender annual, generally about 6 in. high. Leaves opposite. Of pastures. Cultivated flax or linseed (*L. usitatíssimum, most familiar*) was cultivated by early civilizations and its origin is obscure, for it has never been found truly wild. In Britain an occasional weed of cultivation. It is an annual with unbranched stems about 18 in. high bearing large rich blue flowers.

MALLOW FAMILY: *Malváceae*

A family of herbs, shrubs, and trees found usually in the warm parts of the world.

In Britain, herbs of rather coarse texture having alternate palmately veined leaves. Sepals five, united, bearing sepal-like bracts at their base. Petals five, separate. The filaments of the stamens are united in a tube around the pistil.

In gardens are found *Abútilon* from S. America and *Hibíscus,* mostly from warm climates; the tree-mallows (*Lavatéra*), one kind of which (*L. abórea, tree-like*) is a rare native, from S. Europe, and the holly-hock (*Althaéa rósea, rose-coloured*) brought from the Mediterranean region in the sixteenth century.

75. COMMON MALLOW, *Málva sylvéstris, wild.* Summer.

Biennial or annual with several branching stems about 3 ft. high.

The whole plant is hairy. Flowers lilac-pink, showy. The anthers ripen and shed their pollen immediately the flower opens, then they wither and the styles protrude beyond them to receive pollen from other opening flowers. This prevents self-pollination. Of waysides, waste places, and as a garden weed.

76. DWARF MALLOW, *Málva rotundifólia, round-leafed.* Summer to autumn.

Perennial with prostrate, downy stems, about 1 ft. high, much

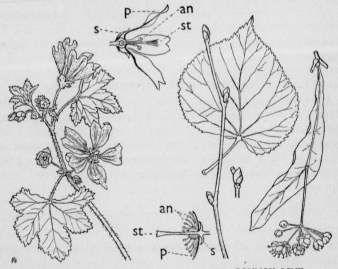

75. COMMON MALLOW   77. COMMON LIME

smaller than the above. Anthers and stigmas ripen at the same time. Of similar situations to the last. Musk-mallow (*M. moschata, musk*) has deeply cut stem leaves which have a faint musk scent when rubbed. Name from Greek *malake,* soft, alluding to the emollient qualities of the plant, which may easily be tested by chewing a leaf.

LIME FAMILY: *Tiliáceae*

A family, nearly all trees or shrubs, found chiefly in S.-E. Asia and Brazil, represented in Britain by *Tília* or lime, alone. (The fruit called lime is no relative, but belongs to the lemon genus, *Cítrus.*)

77. COMMON LIME or LINDEN, *Tília vulgáris, common.* Summer.

The commonest lime in Britain, and of hybrid origin. The tree is easily recognized by the twiggy knobs or *burrs* on the stem. The flower is greenish-yellow, sweetly scented, and a valuable source of nectar for bees. The inner bark is very tough, and until replaced by raffia was used for making 'bast' for tying. The timber is white and soft, and used for indoor work, particularly carving and turned work (Text Fig. 77).

GERANIUM FAMILY: *Geraniáceae*

A cosmopolitan family, nearly all herbs.

In Britain, annual or perennial herbs, usually with deeply cut or compound leaves. Sepals and petals, five. The ovary is five-lobed and five-celled, the long styles being attached to a central axis, hence the names crane's-bill and heron's-bill.

The florist's 'geraniums' are in reality species of *Pelargónium* from the Cape and elsewhere and belong to this family. The 'nasturtiums,' species and florists' forms of *Tropaeólum* from S. America, are closely related. So are the balsams (*Impátiens*), one or two species of which are found naturalized in this country; they have spurred flowers, a powerful, somewhat aromatic scent and the ripe fruit shoot their seeds out violently when touched.

78. WOOD CRANE'S-BILL, *Geránium sylváticum, of woods.* Summer.

Perennial, reaching 3 ft., with large rounded five- or seven-lobed leaves, deeply cut, of moist woods and fields in the north. The meadow crane's-bill (*G. praténse, of meadows*) has more deeply cut leaves, larger and blue flowers, and is usually a taller plant than the last. Of moist situations in the south.

79. HERB ROBERT, *Geránium Robertiánum.* Spring to autumn.

An erect or rather spreading, branching annual, 1 ft. or more high. The stems usually red. Leaves divided into finely cut leaflets. Flowers small, purplish-pink coloured. Of stony waste places (Text Fig. 79); inset shows the ripe fruit and the method by which the seed is catapulted.

80. DOVE'S-FOOT CRANE'S-BILL, *Geránium mólle, soft.* Spring to early autumn.

An annual with weak, hairy, spreading stems up to 1 ft. long.

Radical leaves on long stalks, rounded, divided into seven or more
lobes, which are again lobed. Of wastes and fields. Two rather
similar but rarer species may be mistaken for this; neither has the
notched petals of G. *mólle*.

81. CUT-LEAVED CRANE'S-BILL, *Geránium disséctum, cut-up.* Spring
   to summer.

   An annual, rather similar to No. 80 in growth, but distinguished by

   79. HERB ROBERT   84. HORSE-CHESTNUT

the leaves, cut into five or more narrow segments which are in turn
lobed. Of dry fields and wastes. Name from Greek *geranos*, a crane,
referring to the beak-like appearance of the fruit.

82. COMMON or HEMLOCK STORK'S-BILL, *Eródium cicutárium, hemlock.*
   Spring to summer.

   Usually an annual with hairy stems up to 1 ft. long. The hairy
compound leaves are aromatic. Of waste land, waysides, and dry
commons, particularly near the sea. The sea stork's-bill (*E. marítimum,
of the sea*) is a rarer plant of the sea coast. It is a small annual, with
hairy, viscid, small, and simple leaves, and reddish-purple flowers.

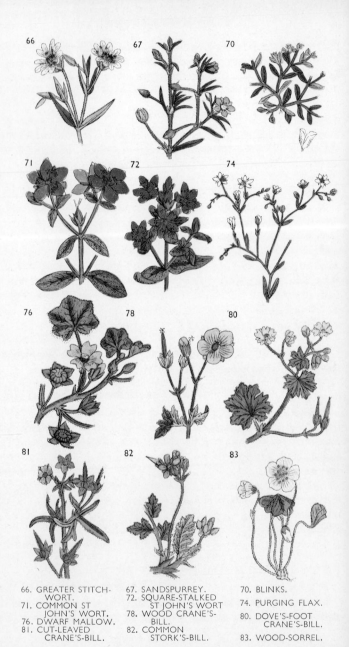

66. GREATER STITCH-
    WORT.
71. COMMON ST
    JOHN'S WORT.
76. DWARF MALLOW.
81. CUT-LEAVED
    CRANE'S-BILL.

67. SANDSPURREY.
72. SQUARE-STALKED
    ST JOHN'S WORT
78. WOOD CRANE'S-
    BILL.
82. COMMON
    STORK'S-BILL.

70. BLINKS.

74. PURGING FLAX.

80. DOVE'S-FOOT
    CRANE'S-BILL.

83. WOOD-SORREL.

Name from Greek *erodios*, heron, alluding to the long beak-like fruit. *Erodium* has pinnately veined, *Geranium* palmately veined, leaves, a feature which always distinguishes these two rather similar genera.

WOOD-SORREL FAMILY: *Oxalidáceae*

A family, nearly all perennial herbs, found chiefly in tropical and sub-tropical climates, and represented in Britain by the following species alone. Sometimes included with the Geranium family.

83. WOOD-SORREL, *Óxalis Acetosélla*. Early to late spring.

A perennial with creeping knotted and rooting stems, growing in woods. The three leaflets forming the leaf 'close,' or droop close to their stalk, at night and in bad weather. The flower has five sepals and petals. The sharp taste of the plant is due to the presence of oxalic acid; the name, referring to this taste, is from Greek *oxus*, acid, and *halos*, salt. It is said that this plant, and not clover, is the original Irish shamrock.

HORSE-CHESTNUT FAMILY: *Hippocastanáceae*

A small family of trees and shrubs, with no native British representatives. Often placed in the family *Sapindáceae*.

84. HORSE-CHESTNUT, *Aésculus Hippocastánum*. Late spring.

A large deciduous tree planted for ornament alone, the white timber being comparatively little used, as it is very soft. In winter, easily recognized by its large pointed sticky buds. The flowers, in showy spikes, are white marked with pink and yellow. The fruit, capsules and not true nuts, are known as 'conquers' or 'cobblers' (Text Fig. 84). A native of N. Greece and Albania, where it is rather scarce, it was introduced to England early in the seventeenth century. Several other kinds are grown, particularly a red-flowered hybrid. It is not related to the sweet or Spanish chestnut (No. 390).

MAPLE FAMILY: *Aceráceae*

A family of north temperate deciduous trees and shrubs.
Leaves opposite, without stipules; often, but not invariably, palmately lobed. Flowers usually with four or five petals, in racemes or

corymbs. Fruit a 'key,' consisting of two winged lobes joined at their base. The wings help seed-dispersal.

85. COMMON or HEDGEROW MAPLE, *Ácer campéstre, of the plains.* Spring.

A rather small, round-headed, deciduous tree, but often found as a shrub in hedgerows. Leaves palmately veined and lobed. Wings of fruit horizontal. Timber little, if at all, used.

86. SYCAMORE (PLANE of Scotland), *Ácer Pseúdo-plátanus.* Spring.

A large deciduous tree, one of the hardiest, most adaptable, and prolific trees in Britain, although probably not a true native. Leaves usually five-lobed, up to 7 in. across. The hard, white wood is used for furniture and cabinet-making. The plane-tree proper (*Plátanus*) is sometimes confused with the sycamore owing to a similarity in the leaf; it is, however, no relative, belonging to the plane family (*Platanáceae*), which has no native British representatives. The London plane (*P. acerifólia, maple-leaved*), of obscure hybrid origin, is one of the trees most often found, usually thriving, in towns. It is easily identified by the dark-coloured bark, which peels in big flakes around the stem, and the seed-vessels in the form of hanging balls remaining on the tree after the leaves fall. When they break, a fine, hairy dust is produced affecting (it is said) people prone to hay-fever and bronchial trouble. Timber little, if at all, used.

Several kinds of maple are cultivated, particularly the Norway maple (*A. platanoídes, plane-like*) and its varieties, having five-lobed leaves, heart-shaped at the base, and noticeable erect corymbs of greenish-yellow flowers open before the leaves. Numerous forms of the small Japanese maple (*A. palmátum, palmate*) are also grown. The sap of maples is often free-flowing and syrupy; that of the sugar-maple (*A. sacchárum, sugar*) of eastern N. America supplies maple syrup.

HOLLY FAMILY: *Aquifoliáceae*

A family of shrubs and trees spread over the world, but limited in Britain to the following:

87. HOLLY, *Ílex Aquifólium.* Early summer.

Usually an evergreen shrub or small tree (occasionally reaching 80 ft.) with dark green leaves, sometimes smooth and entire (particularly on the upper branches) but mostly waved and spiny. Male and female flowers, the calyx with four or five teeth and the corolla with a similar number of petals, are usually on separate trees. Fruit a bright-red or sometimes yellow drupe. Wood, white, occasionally used in cabinet work. Bird-lime was prepared from the inner bark. The holly has been cultivated in gardens for centuries, especially in hedges. It has produced numerous sports and hybrids, such as the silver, golden, and weeping forms.

SPINDLE-TREE FAMILY: *Celastráceae*

A fairly large family of trees and shrubs growing mostly in tropical or warm climates, but represented by one species alone in Britain. Certain hardy kinds of *Celástrus*, climbers from N. America and China, are sometimes cultivated.

88. SPINDLE-TREE, *Euónymus europaéus, European*. Spring to early summer.

A deciduous shrub or small tree, with opposite, lance-shaped, un-divided but slightly toothed leaves. Flowers yellowish-green, pod a brilliant red with orange seeds. Wood hard, and formerly used for making skewers and spindles. Several foreign kinds, some ever-green, are found in gardens (Text Fig. 88).

BUCKTHORN FAMILY: *Rhamnáceae*

A large cosmopolitan family, mostly trees, shrubs, and climbers, represented in Britain only by the buckthorns. It includes the N. American *Ceanóthus*, of which some species and several hybrids are cultivated.

The commonest buckthorn is the alder buckthorn (*Rhámnus Frángula*), a hedgerow shrub or small tree, with alternate leaves, oval and generally pointed. Young twigs have the look of an alder about them, but the alder is easily identified by its ever-present catkins. The flower, in summer, is small and greenish-white. Fruit, a berry, at first green, then red, and black when ripe. As charcoal, the wood is used for gunpowder. Most have a purging quality, a N. American kind produces *Cascara sagrada*.

PEA FAMILY: *Leguminósae*

One of the largest families, with some 12,000 species of herbs, trees, and shrubs spread over the world.

The British representatives belong to the sub-family *Papilionatae*. The distinctive flower is described on page 8 and Plate II. The fruit is a one-celled pod, or *legume*, which gives its name to the family.

Economically it is important, producing valuable food plants. Of numerous introduced genera grown in Britain the following may be mentioned: the locust-trees (*Robinia*) from N. America, often wrongly called acacias, the commonest kind having been once advocated as a timber tree, but now not used as such; the Judas-tree (*Cércis Siliquástrum*) from S. Europe; the honey-locust (*Gledítschia triacánthos, three-spined*) from N. America; bladder-senna (*Colútea*) and Spanish broom (*Spártium juncéum, rush-like*), shrubs from S. Europe; the tree-lupin (*Lúpinus arbóreus, tree-like*) from California and the florists' lupins, which are hybrids from N. American parents; runner and dwarf beans (*Phaseólus*) from S. America; the climbing *Wistária* from China; and numerous tender plants from Australia, New Zealand, and elsewhere grown in greenhouses.

Most leguminous plants bear nodules on their roots which assist in storing-up nitrogenous material (a valuable plant food). This peculiarity is valuable to the farmer, who, by growing certain leguminous crops and ploughing them in, enriches his ground.

89. GORSE, FURZE, WHIN, *Úlex europaéus, European.* Spring to summer and intermittently afterwards.

A deciduous shrub, up to 6 ft. or so high, the intricate branches being armed with spines. The flowers are almond-scented. Of commons, heaths, and sandy places. The dwarf furzes, botanically distinct, are smaller, deeper green, and flower only during late summer and autumn. A double-flowered gorse is often seen in gardens.

90. DYER'S GREENWEED, WOADWAXEN, *Genísta tinctória, used for dyeing.* Summer.

A low, spreading, deciduous shrub, without spines, about $1\frac{1}{2}$ ft. high. Of fields and waste places. Once used for making the dye Kendal green.

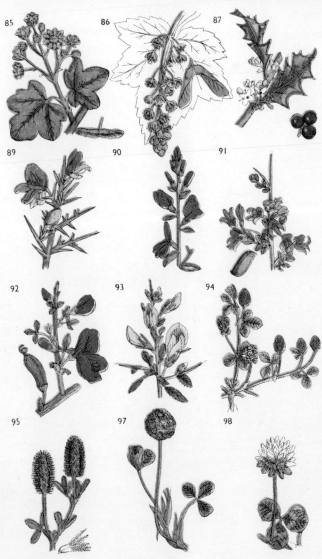

85. COMMON MAPLE. 86. SYCAMORE. 87. HOLLY.
89. GORSE. 90. DYER'S GREEN-WEED. 91. NEEDLE FURZE.
92. COMMON BROOM. 93. REST-HARROW. 94. BLACK MEDICK.
95. HARE'S-FOOT TREFOIL. 97. STRAWBERRY-HEADED CLOVER. 98. WHITE CLOVER.

91. NEEDLE FURZE, NEEDLE WHIN, PETTY WHIN, *Genísta ánglica, English.* Early summer.

A low, straggling, deciduous bush, with woody, spiny branches. Flowers in racemes. Of heaths and moors.

92. COMMON BROOM, *Cýtisus scopárius, a twig-besom.* Spring to early summer.

A shrub up to 6 ft. or so high, with very numerous upright, thin, wiry, and angled branches. Leaves mostly with three leaflets. With-

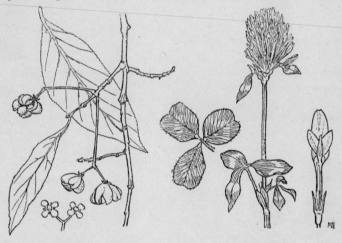

88. SPINDLE-TREE   96. RED CLOVER

out spines. Of dry, waste places. Once important as a drug. Several forms and hybrids are cultivated ornamentally.

93. REST-HARROW, *Onónis spinosa, full of spines.* Summer to early autumn.

A spiny undershrub, rather variable in habit and spininess, some-times spreading and creeping, at others more erect. The seaside prostrate form is distinguished as *O. répens, creeping.* A plant of poor pastures and badly cultivated land; its tough growth and roots make it difficult to harrow, hence the popular name.

94. BLACK MEDICK, NONSUCH CLOVER, *Medicágo lupulína, hop-like.* Spring to autumn.

Sometimes wrongly called hop trefoil, from its likeness to No. 99.

E

A hairy spreading annual. The pod is not enclosed within the calyx as it is in the trefoil, and the leaflets have a projecting mid-rib. Of fields and waste places. Spotted medick (*M. arábica, Arabian*) is an annual with spotted leaves, small yellow flowers, and spiny pods coiled like a snail-shell. Lucerne, alfalfa, or purple medick (*M. satíva, cultivated*) is a perennial cultivated for fodder. Of uncertain origin, it has branching hollow stems up to 3 ft. high, purplish flowers in late summer, a trefoil leaf, and a curled-up pod. Often found as an escape from cultivation.

95. HARE'S-FOOT TREFOIL, *Trifólium arvénse, of cultivated fields*. Summer to early autumn.

An erect, slender annual, branching, up to 1 ft. high. The long calyx teeth give the flower a feathered appearance. Of dry fields and banks.

96. RED or PURPLE CLOVER, *Trifólium praténse, of meadows*. Summer.

A short-lived perennial, with hairy, rather spreading stems up to 2 ft. long. Leaflets usually marked with a whitish band. Flowers reddish-purple, turning brown, remaining erect and enclosing the fruit after fertilization. Of fields, and widely cultivated in selected forms for fodder (Text Fig. 96).

97. STRAWBERRY-HEADED CLOVER, *Trifólium fragiferum, strawberry-bearing*. Summer to autumn.

A creeping perennial. Flowers in a small globose head. After flowering the calyces enlarge and often turn red, giving the appearance of a strawberry. Of dry fields.

98. WHITE or DUTCH CLOVER, *Trifólium répens, creeping*. Spring to autumn.

A creeping perennial. Flowers sometimes pink. Flower-stalks droop after flowering. Found in most good pastures. Probably a comparatively recent introduction to Ireland, yet now generally regarded as the Irish shamrock (see No. 83).

99. HOP-CLOVER, HOP TREFOIL, *Trifólium campéstre, of plains*. Summer.

An annual, much branched, some of the stems trailing while others

are erect. Of dry, gravelly pastures. When fertilized, the inflorescence, looking rather like a hop, turns down on its stalk (Text Fig. 99).

There are many other clovers and trefoils, including kinds such as
Swedish clover or alsike (brought from Sweden in 1834) introduced
and cultivated in pastures. The name *Trifólium* refers to the trefoil leaf
consisting of three leaflets. Another distinguishing feature of the genus

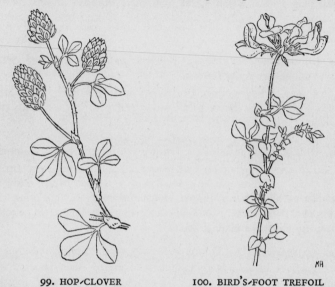

99. HOP-CLOVER   100. BIRD'S-FOOT TREFOIL

is that in most kinds the faded flowers do not fall but remain wrapped
around the fruit.

100. BIRD'S-FOOT TREFOIL, *Lótus corniculátus, horned.* Summer.

A trailing perennial, rather branched, variable in size according to
situation, which may be in wet or dry fields, commons, or heaths. The
flowers in flat umbels are yellow, marked with red. The arrangement
of subsequent pods resembles a bird's claw. It is not a trefoil; two
leaflets at the base of the leaf make a total of five leaflets (Text Fig. 100).

101. KIDNEY VETCH, LADY'S FINGERS, *Anthýllis vulnerária, used for
    curing wounds.* Summer.

A perennial with several spreading stems and often a tuft of radical leaves. The leaves are pinnate, and the plant is hairy. The flower varies in colour. Of dry fields and banks.

102. BIRD'S - FOOT, *Ornithopus perpusillus, very small*. Spring to summer.

A slender, spreading annual, up to 18 in. high. Of dry fields and waste places. Name from Greek, meaning bird's-foot.

103. HORSE-SHOE VETCH, *Hippocrépis comósa, with long tufty hairs*. Spring to summer.

Perennial, branching freely at the base, from 6 in. to 1 ft. high. Of fields and banks on limestone soils in the S., becoming less common in the N. Flowers may be mistaken for bird's-foot trefoil, but otherwise the plant is quite different. The pods form a series of horse-shoe-like shapes; the name, from the Greek, refers to this.

104. TUFTED VETCH, *Vícia Crácca*. Summer.

Perennial, climbing in hedgerows from 2 ft. to 5 ft. high. Flowers bluish-purple. The pod is beaked, about 1 in. long (Text Fig. 104).

105. BUSH VETCH, *Vícia sépium, brown*. Summer.

Perennial with weak, wandering stems up to 3 ft. long. Of hedge-rows, up which the plant straggles.

106. COMMON VETCH, TARE, *Vícia satíva, sown*. Spring to summer.

Annual or biennial with trailing or climbing stems about 2 ft. high. Flowers reddish-purple. The stipules have generally a dark mark in the centre (Text Fig. 106). Two races are cultivated for fodder, and the plant is widely spread in consequence. It is supposed to be a cultivated form of *V. angústifolia, narrow-leaved*, which is similar, but smaller, in all its parts. Both are found in dry fields, open woods, and waste places. The spring vetch (*V. lathyroídes, lathyrus-like*), flowering in spring, is like a miniature *V. satíva*, with stems only a few inches long. It is an annual of fields and waysides.

The annual broad bean of gardens and the beans grown on farms for fodder are kinds of *Vícia* which have undergone many centuries of cultivation and selection—they were well known in Egypt and Greece. Sainfoin (*Onobrýchis viciaefólia, vetch-leaved*) is closely related to the vetches, and is grown as a crop for fodder on dry, barren limestone or chalk fields. It is found wild also, on similar ground. Perennial, up to 2 ft. high. Leaves pinnate, with about twelve pairs of leaflets,

101. KIDNEY VETCH.   102. BIRD'S-FOOT.   103. HORSE-SHOE
105. BUSH VETCH.   107. MEADOW PEA.   VETCH.
110. SLOE.   111. BULLACE.   108. BITTER VETCH.
115. MEADOW-SWEET.   116. DROPWORT.   113. BIRD CHERRY.
                                        117. MOUNTAIN AVENS.

and one at the end.   Flowers in spikes, rose-pink, the wings smaller
than the keel and standard.   Pods spiny.

107. MEADOW PEA, VETCHLING, YELLOW PEA, *Lathýrus praténsis*,
    of meadows.   Summer to early autumn.

Perennial, much branched, with angled stems from underground
runners.   Growth straggling.   Found in moist hedgerows and fields.

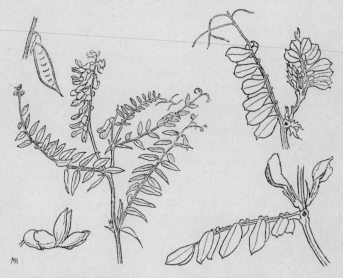

104. TUFTED VETCH   106. COMMON VETCH

108. BITTER VETCH, TUBEROUS PEA, *Lathýrus montánus, of mountains.*
    Spring to early summer.

Perennial, forming small tubers at the root.   The stems up to a foot
high, winged.   Of heaths and open woodland.   The sweet and everlasting peas are exotic, mostly S. European, species and forms of *Lathýrus*.
The green-peas are closely related, being the cultivated forms of *Písum*,
probably originating in S. Europe.

109. COMMON LABURNUM, *Labúrnum anagyroídes, Anágyris - like.*[1]
    Spring to early summer.

A small tree, native of C. and S. Europe and one of the first

----

[1] *Anágyris,* a Mediterranean shrub.

foreign trees to be introduced, possibly in the fourteenth century. Flowers yellow. Improved forms are now often planted. The seeds contain a strong alkaloid poison. The timber is hard, and sometimes used in furniture and cabinet-making.

ROSE FAMILY: *Rosáceae*

A large family of herbs, shrubs, and trees spread all over the world, but particularly in the temperate parts of the N. hemisphere.

Leaves usually alternate with stipules. The flower-type is described on page 8 and Plate III. The fruit is variable in form, often the receptacle of the flower becomes fleshy and surrounds the true fruit; in the apple, for instance, the edible fleshy *false fruit* surrounds the true fruit, which is the 'core' and its 'pips.' The plants frequently spread by means of suckers and rooting runners.

Certain genera produce a high proportion of varieties and natural hybrids. It is generally held that the reason for this is that these genera have not yet become stabilized in the process of evolution. This peculiarity has been used by man for many centuries in the selection of special forms of flower and fruit to satisfy his desires. The origin of the cultivated fruit-trees goes back to the early civilizations, and although much attention has been devoted to the subject recently, it still remains somewhat obscure, though full of interest. This multiplication of forms makes the botanist's task of classification difficult; it is still far from perfect.

The quince (*Cýdonia oblónga, oblong*) from C. Asia has been grown in Britain for centuries; its garden relative, popularly known as the 'japonica,' the Japanese quince (*C. lagenária, bottle-shaped*), is in reality a Chinese plant; the medlar (*Méspilus germánica, German*) is from S.-E. Europe—the fruits are eaten as they begin to decay; many kinds of *Cotóneáster*, coming mostly from the Himalayas and China; the firethorns (*Pyracántha*), which are also largely of Asiatic origin; and the snowy mespilus (*Amelánchier rotundifólia, round-leaved*), a European plant, and many other members of the family are found in gardens.

110. SLOE, BLACKTHORN, *Prúnus spinósa, spiny*. Early spring.

A deciduous suckering shrub or small tree. The small branches often end in a spine. Fruit about ½ in. diameter, very acid. Of hedges and thickets.

111. BULLACE, *Prúnus insititia, grafted or budded.* Spring.

Taller and less spiny than the last. The fruit, black or yellow, is globose and larger. Of hedgerows. A cultivated form is the damson, so called because it has been cultivated around Damascus since pre-Christian times. Some garden plums have also been developed from the bullace. The true wild plum (*P. doméstica, domestic*) is a native of

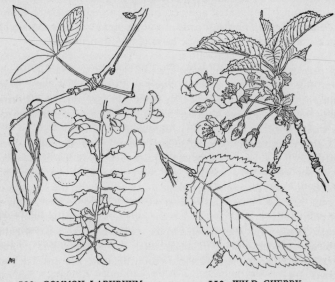

109. COMMON LABURNUM   112. WILD CHERRY

Europe and not Britain; wild plums found are degenerate forms of orchard kinds.

112. WILD CHERRY, GEAN, MAZZARD, *Prúnus Ávium.* Spring.

A deciduous tree, sometimes quite tall, and the commonest wild cherry. Flowers white, separately stalked. Fruit may be bitter or sweet, but never acid (Text Fig. 112). The wild dwarf cherry (*P. Cérasus*) is a freely suckering bush or small tree rather similar to the last. The leaves are not hairy, and the fruit is always acid. It is much less common, and can usually be distinguished by its bushy, suckering form and smaller size. Both are parents of cultivated fruiting cherries; the gean of many of the black forms, the dwarf of the morello type. A double-flowered gean is often seen cultivated ornamentally. The numerous Japanese flowering cherries, of recent introduction, but already very popular in gardens, are the progeny of Asiatic species, which have been developed by the Japanese for their quality of flower. Few bear fruit.

113. BIRD CHERRY, *Prúnus Pádus*. Spring.

A deciduous shrub or tree with fragrant flowers in racemes. The fruit is about ¼ in. diameter and very bitter. In slightly varying forms this tree is found in northern parts of Europe and Asia from Britain to Japan. The timber is said to be of value in cabinet work.

114. COMMON or CHERRY LAUREL, *Prúnus Laurocérasus*. Spring.

Evergreen shrub of vigorous spreading growth when allowed to grow naturally, as is, unfortunately, seldom the case in this country, where it is often cut into hedges or badly planted under trees. Native of E. Europe and Asia Minor; introduced in the seventeenth century. Flowers dull white, scented. Fruit about ½ in. long, dark purple, with a stone. The leaf always has at least two marks (glands) on the underside near the stalk. The clippings should be regarded as poisonous to stock (Text Fig. 114).

The Portugal laurel (*P. lusitánica, Portuguese*) is somewhat similar; it is distinguished by its longer flowerspikes, not flowering till June, and the absence of glands on the leaves. Introduced in the seventeenth century. The socalled 'variegated laurel' is really no relative of the above; it belongs to the dogwood family (see page 77). The laurel of the classics is also unrelated; it is the handsome aromatic evergreen bay laurel (*Laurus nobílis, noble*) from the Mediterranean. It is grown in this country.

Other kinds of Prunus long cultivated in Britain include the almond (*P. commúnis, common*) from S. Europe and the Levant; the peach and nectarine, forms of *P. pérsica, Persian*, which probably originated in China, where they were cultivated long before they were known in Europe; and the apricot (*P. Ármeniaca*), also from China.

115. MEADOWSWEET, QUEEN OF THE MEADOWS, *Spiraéa Úlmaria*. Summer.

Perennial with reddish stems about 3 ft. high. Leaflets whitish beneath. Flowers scented. Of damp meadows, pond and ditch sides.

116. DROPWORT, *Spiraéa Filipéndula*. Summer.

Perennial, rather similar in appearance to the last, but only about

2 ft. high. Flowers unscented. Leaflets greenish beneath and more numerous. Of dry pastures, downs, and heaths, particularly on lime soils. Both these spiraeas were once much valued for their tonic bitter qualities.

117. MOUNTAIN AVENS, WHITE DRYAS, *Drýas octopétala, eight-petalled.* Summer.

A perennial, prostrate shrub-like plant. Leaves white and downy

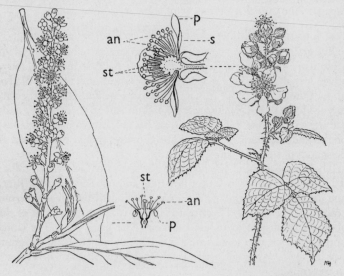

114. CHERRY LAUREL   121. BLACKBERRY

beneath—very crinkled on the edges. Seed feathery. Of mountains in the N. and W.

118. COMMON AVENS, HERB-BENNET, *Géum urbánum, of the town.* Summer.

Perennial, stems up to 3 ft. high. Of hedgerows, wood- and road-sides. Seed-heads feathery, the seeds having a hook to help distribution. Bennet is said to be a contraction of St Benedict.

119. WATER AVENS, *Géum rivále, of the brook.* Spring to summer.

Perennial, rather similar to above but smaller, with more hairy leaves and larger flowers. Of marshes and ditches, in the N. and E., rare in the S./W. The roots of avens have the scent and taste of cloves, and to this is attributed the name *Geum*, from the Greek *geuo*, to taste or smell.

120. WILD RASPBERRY, *Rúbus Idaéus*. Spring to early summer.

Perennial with creeping rootstock. The stems are biennial. The fruit is sometimes yellow in cultivated forms; when ripe it comes away from the receptacle. A parent, with N. American and continental kinds, of the cultivated raspberry. Of woods and heaths; often de/generate forms escaped from cultivation.

121. BLACKBERRY, BRAMBLE, *Rúbus fruticósus, shrubby*. Late spring to summer.

A perennial deciduous shrub. Stems very prickly, of two or three years' duration, arching, and often rooting when they touch the ground. Of hedgerows, woods, banks, etc. The fruit is firmly attached to the receptacle. The flowers vary in size and colour from white to pink (Text Fig. 121).

122. DEWBERRY, *Rúbus caésius, bluish/grey*. Summer.

Rather similar to the above, but with more slender stems, covered with a whitish bloom when young. These spread along the ground. The flowers are few, and the fruit has only a few large pips. It is also covered with bloom—which gives the name *caesius*.

The above three *Rubi* are the three principal kinds; it is a very variable genus, and one authority has divided the British representa/tives alone into one hundred and three species.

The fruit consists of a number of united little drupes, each one similar to a cherry.

The loganberry is a hybrid between a garden raspberry and a garden blackberry. It was raised in California in 1881.

123. WILD STRAWBERRY, *Fragária vésca, edible*. Spring to autumn.

A perennial which sends out runners. These root at their joints and form new plants. Of woodland, hedgerows, and shady banks. A parent in one form of the dessert strawberry, which, as we know it to/day, was not produced till 1806.

124. BARREN STRAWBERRY, STRAWBERRY/LEAVED POTENTILLA, *Potentílla stérilis, sterile*. Early spring.

In appearance and flower not unlike a strawberry; it does not send out long runners, however, and the fruit does not swell up. Of banks, dry fields, and open woodlands.

125. CINQUEFOIL, *Potentilla réptans, creeping.* Summer to autumn.

A perennial with slender creeping stems, rooting at the joints. The leaves, all stalked, consist of five leaflets forming the cinquefoil. Of grassland and roadsides.

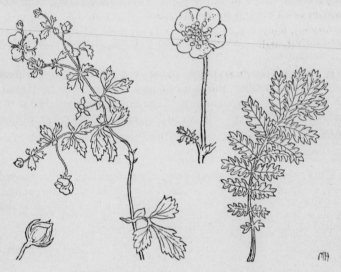

126. TORMENTIL   127. SILVER-WEED

126. TORMENTIL, *Potentilla erécta, upright.* Summer.

Perennial, much like a smaller form of the above, but the leaves nearly always have three leaflets, and on the upper part of the stem are stalkless. Flower bright yellow. Of dry fields, banks, heaths, etc. (Text Fig. 126).

127. SILVER-WEED, GOOSE-WEED, *Potentilla Anserína.* Summer.

Perennial, with long runners which root at the joints. Leaves densely covered with silvery-grey hairs on the underside. Flower yellow. Of roadsides, fields, and, because of its running habits, a troublesome garden weed (Text Fig. 127).

128. MARSH CINQUEFOIL, *Potentílla palústris, of marshes*. Summer.

A perennial with stems, often purple, up to 18 in. high. The fruit resembles a strawberry. Name from Latin *potens*, powerful, some kinds once having a reputation as powerful drugs. The potentillas have a double calyx, with an outer ring of lobes (see inset, Text Fig. 126).

129. LADY'S-MANTLE, *Alchemílla vulgáris, common*. Spring to summer.

Perennial, from 6 in. to 1 ft. high. Leaves always green. Of moist meadows and stream-sides. Alpine lady's-mantle (*A. alpina, of high mountains*), found among the mountains of Scotland and N. England, is similar though smaller and covered with silvery hairs.

130. FIELD LADY'S-MANTLE, PARSLEY PIERT, *Alchemilla arvénsis, of cultivated fields*. Spring to summer.

A small annual, branched and spreading, a few inches high, and covered with soft hairs. A weed of arable land and on gravel soils. Both this and the last were old medicines, the first having tonic properties.

131. SALAD BURNET, *Potérium Sanguisórba*. Summer.

Perennial up to 1 ft. high. The lower flowers are male with their anthers hanging out, the upper female bearing a long style with a tufted stigma. Of dry fields in limestone districts. Once a medicine prescribed for varied complaints. The leaves have a cucumber taste and are sometimes used in salads and drinks. The name, from the Greek *poterion*, cup, is usually connected with this use.

132. AGRIMONY, *Agrimónia Eupatória*. Summer.

A perennial up to 3 ft. high, covered with soft hairs. Fruit forms a burr. Of waysides and the edges of fields. Once used medicinally as a tonic, and still employed in herb beers.

133. SCOTCH or BURNET ROSE, *Rósa spinosíssima, most spiny*. Spring to early summer.

A low bush up to 4 ft. high but usually less. Stems much branched, covered with thin spines and bristles mixed. Fruit dark, usually almost black when ripe. Of wastes and dry heaths among hills and by the sea, particularly in the N. The origin of the cultivated Scotch roses.

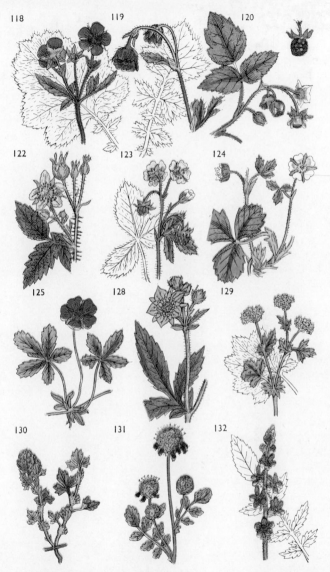

118. COMMON AVENS.
122. DEWBERRY.
125. CINQUEFOIL.
130. FIELD LADY'S-
    MANTLE.

119. WATER AVENS.
123. WILD STRAW-
    BERRY.
128. MARSH CINQUEFOIL.
131. SALAD BURNET.

120. WILD RASPBERRY.
124. BARREN STRAW-
    BERRY.
129. LADY'S-MANTLE.
132. AGRIMONY.

134. DOG ROSE, *Rósa canína, dog.* Early summer.

A vigorous suckering shrub up to 12 ft. high. The stems armed with even, hooked prickles, unmixed with bristles. Flowers scented. Of the five sepals or calyx lobes, one is pinnately divided on both sides, two on one side only, and the fifth undivided. One of the commonest and most beautiful hedgerow shrubs, and usually the best stock on which to bud garden roses.

The rose is typical of its family in being a very variable plant, and botanists still fail to agree in its classification.

Of other native species the sweetbriar (*R. rubinósa, rusty*) is identified by its sweetly scented foliage, particularly noticeable after a summer shower. It is the old eglantine. The Ayrshire (a misleading name as it is least common in Scotland) or field rose (*R. arvénsis, of cultivated fields*) is rather similar to the dog rose, but is distinguished by its very thin, trailing stems. Of the garden roses, their origins and history, innumerable volumes have already been written. They were cultivated in Greece as long ago as the fifth century B.C. A modern hybrid rose may have ancestors from C. Europe, Persia, N. America, or China.

135. WILD PEAR-TREE, *Pýrus commúnis, common.* Spring.

A deciduous bush or small tree of the pyramidal form typical in garden pears, of whose many varieties it is the parent. The *spurs* (short flowering branches) often bear spines. Possibly not truly native of Britain; the wild pear found in woodlands or hedgerows is usually a degenerate seedling of cultivated forms.

136. WILD APPLE, *Málus pumíla, dwarf.* Spring.

A small deciduous tree with a rounded head and somewhat weeping branches, the trunk often crooked. Probably a British native, but plants found in woodlands and hedgerows are often degenerate forms seeded from the cultivated apple, of which it is a parent.

137. WHITE BEAM, *Sórbus Ária.* Spring.

A deciduous shrub or tree of erect growth. The under-surface of the leaves and the young shoots are covered with white felt. The twigs lose this, becoming smooth and dark-brown in winter, marked with pale warts. Flowers scented. A typical tree of chalk hills.

138. ROWAN-TREE, MOUNTAIN ASH, *Sórbus Aucupária.* Spring to
early summer.

A deciduous tree, erect when young, but with a spreading top when
mature. Flowers and fruits in showy corymbs. The service tree
(*S. domestica, of the house*) is usually a small or middle-sized tree. Leaves
compoundly pinnate, as in the last. Flowers white, in panicles; fruit
pear-shaped, 1 in. long, edible when starting to rot. Native of Europe.

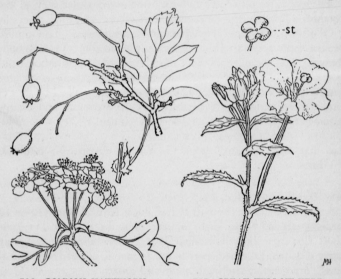

139. COMMON HAWTHORN   141. GREAT WILLOW-HERB

The wild service (*S. torminális, relieving colic*) is a native tree found mostly
in the S. Leaves simple, three- or four-lobes. Flowers white in
loose corymbs; fruit brownish-coloured, egg-shaped, about ½ in. long.

139. COMMON HAWTHORN, MAY, *Crataégus monógyna, with one style.*
Spring to early summer.

Hawthorns in Britain consist of two distinct species, this, usually
the commoner and larger tree, with one style, and *C. Oxyacántha* which
has two or three styles in the flower. Both are deciduous shrubs or
small trees, gnarled and leaning when old. Flowers white and
scented, opening perhaps on the May-day of the old, but not the
present calendar (Text Fig. 139). Pink and double forms of *Crataé-*

gus are cultivated, as well as N. American species. A valuable hedge plant, as such, called *quick-set*.

WILLOW-HERB FAMILY: *Onagráceae*

For the most part a family of herbs, found all over the world, but particularly in N. America.

In Britain, herbs. Leaves usually opposite without stipules, and toothed. The parts of the flowers are in fours or twos. Fruit a capsule.

The N. American evening primroses (*Oenothéra*) form an extensive genus; several are common in gardens. *Oe. Lamárckiana*, a biennial with stems about 3 ft. high bearing large, sweetly scented, pale yellow flowers which open towards evening in late summer, is often found naturalized, particularly along river-banks. The *Fúchsia*, a S. American plant introduced at the end of the eighteenth century, and *Clárkia* from N. America, also belong to this family.

140. FRENCH WILLOW-HERB, ROSE-BAY, *Epilóbium angustifólium, narrow-leaved.* Summer.

A perennial with a creeping rootstock. Stems usually little branched, not hairy, up to 4 ft. high. Stigma, four-lobed. The flowers, in racemes, open widely; in other willow-herbs they remain more or less bell-shaped; they appear to be on long stalks, which are really ovaries (inset Text Fig. 142). These split when ripe, and the seeds, each with a tuft of down, are carried away by the wind. A plant of open woodland, often creeping over large areas. Frequently seen naturalized on waste land near towns. Though handsome, it should not be planted in gardens, as it becomes a troublesome and prolific weed.

141. GREAT WILLOW-HERB, CODLINS-AND-CREAM, *Epilóbium hirsútum, hairy.* Summer.

A perennial with branched stems up to 5 ft. high. The whole plant is hairy. The handsome flowers are rose shading to white in the centre. Of river-sides and ditches, not common in the N. The leaves when crushed smell of apple-pie (Text Fig. 141).

142. BROAD-LEAVED WILLOW-HERB, *Epilóbium montánum, of mountains.* Summer.

Perennial, up to 1 ft. high, but very variable in size according to situation. Flowers rose-coloured, with a four-lobed stigma. Wide-spread in waste places and as a garden weed (Text Fig. 142). Of the other willow-herbs, the square-stemmed (*E. tetragónum, four-angled*), a perennial about 2 ft. high with markedly angular stems and a club-shaped stigma, is common in ditches and moist places. Hoary willow-herb (*E. parviflóra, small-flowered*) is another troublesome weed. It is

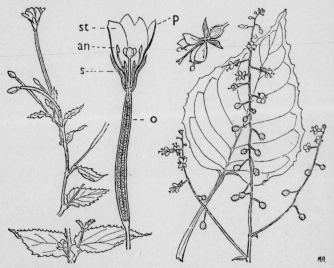

142. BROAD-LEAVED WILLOW-HERB   143. ENCHANTER'S NIGHTSHADE

very similar to No. 142, but is rather downy all over, and has most of its leaves alternate.

143. ENCHANTER'S NIGHTSHADE, *Circaéa lutetiána, of Lutetia (Paris)*. Summer.

A perennial with a creeping rootstock and upright square stems about 1½ ft. long. Flowers pinkish-white. The fruits become bristly and are caught and carried about by the fur of animals (Text Fig. 143).

LOOSESTRIFE FAMILY: *Lythráceae*

A family of herbs, shrubs and trees spread over the world. In Britain all are herbs. The lower leaves are simple and opposite.

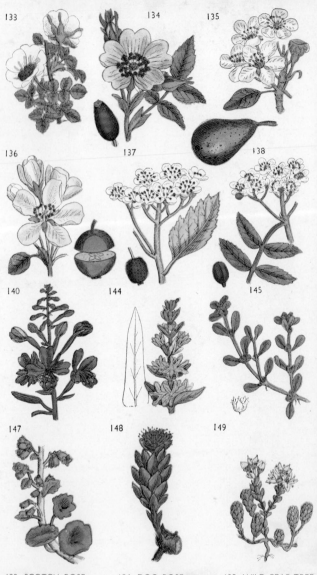

133. SCOTCH ROSE.
136. WILD APPLE.
140. FRENCH
       WILLOW-HERB.
147. WALL PENNY-
       WORT.

134. DOG ROSE.
137. WHITE BEAM.
144. PURPLE LOOSE-
       STRIFE.
148. ROSE-ROOT.

135. WILD PEAR-TREE.
138. ROWAN-TREE.
145. WATER PURS-
       LANE.
149. ENGLISH STONE-
       CROP.

Sepals are joined in a tube having from four to six teeth, and the same number of smaller outer teeth. Petals from four to six, rarely none. Fruit a capsule.

144. PURPLE LOOSESTRIFE, *Lýthrum Salicária*. Summer.

Perennial, with strong stems 3 ft. or more high. Leaves opposite or in threes. The flowers in thick showy spikes, of different types on different plants, varying in the relative lengths of stamens and styles and in the structure of the pollen grains. This arrangement allows eighteen possible methods of fertilization, only a limited number of which are, however, fully effective in producing fertile seed. Of stream-sides and wet places. Name from Greek *luthron*, blood, alluding to the flower-colour. *Lysimáchia* (No. 275) is also called loosestrife, but is no relative.

145. WATER PURSLANE, *Péplis Pórtula*. Summer.

An annual, only an inch or two high, branching and creeping, rooting as it goes. Flowers usually petal-less. Forming mats on mud and in damp places.

GOURD OR CUCUMBER FAMILY: *Cucurbitáceae*

A family of herbs, mostly annual climbers with tendrils, of very rapid growth, found principally in tropical and sub-tropical regions, especially Africa.

Leaves alternate, palmately veined. Male and female flowers separate but on the same plant. Fruit fleshy and berry-like.

Bryónia alone is native of Britain, but the gourds and vegetable-marrow (species of *Cucúrbita* of American origin); melons (*Cucúmis Mélo*), originating from Asia, and cucumbers (*Cucúmis sativus, cultivated*), both of which have been so long cultivated that their true origins are rather obscure, are common in gardens.

146. WHITE BRYONY, *Bryónia dioíca, dioecious*. Summer.

A perennial throwing up long annual stems from a tuberous root-stock, which climb by their long tendrils. The flowers (male figured with leaf, female inset *a*) are greenish-white. The ripe berry is red. Of hedgerows, not common N. of the midlands. The roots and berries contain a strong irritant poison. Name from Greek *bruo*, to

F

shoot, alluding to the rapid growth (Text Fig. 146). No relative of black bryony (No. 421).

STONECROP FAMILY: *Crassuláceae*

A large and widespread family of 'succulents' usually inhabiting dry places, particularly abundant in S. Africa.

A succulent plant is one in which the leaves and often stems are swollen and fleshy, and normally full of fluid. They are so formed to

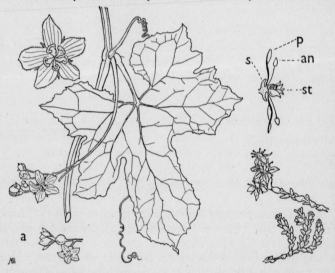

146. WHITE BRYONY   150. STONECROP

conserve the plant's water supply, for succulents grow in deserts, rocky ground, or other situations where fresh water is scarce for long periods. Plants growing under the influence of salt water, which is virtually useless to them as a water supply, often develop a succulent tendency. Succulents are often wrongly called cacti, many having the appearance of a cactus. But a succulent must belong to the family *Cactáceae* (found almost entirely in the New World alone, but widely spread abroad by man) to justify the name cactus.

In Britain, herbs with fleshy leaves, usually alternate. Flowers with five or six sepals and petals, in terminal panicles or cymes. Fruit a number of pods.

The house-leeks (*Sempervivum*), a rosette-plant of mountains, often grown in rockeries, and the bedding-out *Echevéria* from America, are members of the family.

147. WALL PENNYWORT, NAVELWORT, PENNY-PIES, *Cotylédon Umbílicus*. Summer.

Perennial with stems up to 1 ft. long, growing in walls or among rocks, common in the mild and moist counties. Name from Greek *kotule*, a cup, referring to the depression in the centre of the leaf.

148. ROSE-ROOT, *Sédum róseum, rosy*. Summer.

Perennial, with a woody rootstock (smelling of roses when dry) and stems up to 1 ft. long. Male and female flowers normally on separate plants. Found on rocks in the Welsh and N. mountains, and often in old gardens.

149. ENGLISH STONECROP, *Sédum ánglicum, English*. Summer.

Perennial, seldom above an inch or two high, forming dense mats on rocks and banks by the sea, particularly along the west coast.

150. STONECROP, WALL-PEPPER, *Sédum ácre, sharp to the tongue*. Summer.

A procumbent perennial forming mats an inch or two high. Leaves biting to the taste. Flowers bright yellow. Of dry rocks, banks, old walls, etc. (Text Fig. 150). In gardens, these small-leaved sedums may be very troublesome, as the smallest bit broken off will root. Name from Latin *sedeo*, I sit, alluding to the typical squat habit of growth.

SAXIFRAGE FAMILY: *Saxifragáceae*

For the most part a family of herbs found in temperate climates, a number being mountain plants, and some shrubs and trees.

In Britain herbs with leaves often palmately lobed, without stipules. Sepals united, five. Petals separate, five (in *Chrysosplénium*, No. 154, four and none respectively). Fruit a capsule.

The family includes the mock-orange (*Philadélphus coronárius, garland-like*), popularly called syringa, which is really the botanical name of the lilac (page 105), introduced from S.-E. Europe in the sixteenth century; the *Deútzias* from C. and E. Asia; the *Hýdrangeas*

from Asia and N. America (the popular hydrangea of con-
servatories, *H. horténsis, of gardens*, was introduced from China, where
it had been long cultivated, in 1789); and the *Escallónias* from Chile.

It includes, too, the wild gooseberry (*Ríbes Grossulária*), and species
of wild currant (*R. rúbrum, red*) found growing truly wild in the N.
They may be recognized by their likeness to the cultivated forms—
which themselves produce seedlings of a degenerate type which often
appear to be wild.

151. YELLOW MOUNTAIN SAXIFRAGE, *Saxífraga aizoídes, Aizoon-
like*.[1] Summer to autumn.

A perennial with stems about 6 in. high.   Leaves thick and smooth.
Of wet places in the N. mountains and in Ireland.

152. MEADOW SAXIFRAGE, *Saxífraga gránulata, with the root divided
into little knots*.   Spring to early summer.

A perennial up to 1 ft. high.   The stem produces a number of little
'bulbs' at its base, which help to increase the plant.   Of dry fields
and banks.

153. RUE-LEAVED or THREE-FINGERED SAXIFRAGE, *Saxífraga
tridactylítes, three-fingered*.   Spring to early summer.

An annual, about 4 in. high, forming a small rosette of leaves which
have finger-like lobes.   The plant is covered with sticky hairs, and is
found on old walls, and in stony places.

The purple saxifrage (*S. oppositifólia, opposite-leaved*), a very small
cushion-forming plant covered in spring with purple flowers, is found
high up on mountains.   London pride (*S. umbrosa*), found in S.-W.
Ireland, and introduced from Spain and Portugal, has been grown
in gardens for centuries.   Recently, numerous other species of saxifrage
have been introduced to rock gardens.   *Saxífraga*, from the Latin
saxum, a rock, and *frango*, to break, refers to the rock-loving habits of
many kinds.

154. GOLDEN SAXIFRAGE, *Chrysosplénium oppositifólium, opposite-
leaved*.   Late spring.

Perennial, with creeping and rooting stems, up to 5 in. high.   Of
damp, shady places.

[1] *Saxífraga Aizóon,* a continental plant.

155. GRASS OF PARNASSUS, *Parnássia palústris, of marshes.* Late summer to autumn.

Perennial, stems 6 in. to 1 ft. high. The fertilization of the flower is interesting: the four stigmas, sitting directly on the ovary, are surrounded by five anthers which are folded over them. These alternate with five modified anthers, which are fringed and bear at their tips a spot of nectar, on the side near to the stigma. In turn, each of the five

155. GRASS OF PARNASSUS   156. SUNDEW

proper anthers, with pollen on the side remote from the stigmas, ripens, and rises up, liberating its pollen on insects which are attracted by the nectar. These transfer it to the stigmas of other flowers that they visit. When all the anthers have turned back, the stigmas, hitherto unripe, mature (all risk of fertilization of the flower from its own pollen being now past) and receive pollen from other flowers. This odd and complex process is designed to ensure cross-pollination (Text Fig. 155).

SUNDEW FAMILY: *Droseráceae*

A family of bog plants spread widely over the world, all insectivorous, and mostly perennial.

In Britain restricted to *Drósera*, easily identified by the tentacle-like hairs on the leaves, each tipped with a spot of sticky fluid.

156. COMMON SUNDEW, *Drósera rotundifólia, round-leaved*.   Summer to autumn.

A small hairy plant, with rosettes of reddish-coloured leaves. Flower-stems up to 6 in. high, bearing minute white flowers which only open in sunshine.   Of peat bogs and damp, sandy heaths, usually growing in colonies.   Struggling flies caught by the sticky fluid irritate the leaf-hairs, which then curve over their victim; the leaf rolls up, and the fly is slowly dissolved by the juices of the plant.   The narrow-leaved sundew (*D. longifólia, long-leaved*) is often found growing with the above.   The flower-stems are shorter, and the leaf is shown at inset *a* (Text Fig. 156).   Name from the Greek *droseros*, dew, referring to the dewy tips of the leaf-hairs.

WATER MILFOIL FAMILY: *Haloragidáceae*

A family of land, marsh, or water herbs distributed over the world, but particularly in Australia.

In Britain, aquatic herbs with opposite or whorled leaves and insignificant, usually unisexual, flowers.   Fruit, nutlets.

157. WATER MILFOIL, *Myriophýllum spicátum, spiked*.   Summer.

Perennial, creeping and rooting under water, the stems reaching to the surface.   Leaves very finely cut.   Male flowers usually at the top, female at the bottom, of the flower-spike, which is raised above water. Of still and sluggish water.   Whorled milfoil (*M. verticillatum, whorled*) is similar in appearance, but except in shallow water, the flowers are under the surface.   Name from Greek *myrios*, many, and *phyllon*, leaf.

MARE'S-TAIL FAMILY: *Hippuridáceae*

A family including only the following, which is almost cosmopolitan.

158. MARE'S-TAIL, *Hippúris vulgáris, common*.   Summer.

Rather similar to No. 157, but the leaves are narrow and not cut. The stems project up to ¾ ft. above water, and bear minute flowers. Of shallow ponds.   Name from Greek *hippos*, horse, and *oura*, tail. Not to be confused with the horsetails (*Equisetáceae*) on page 170.

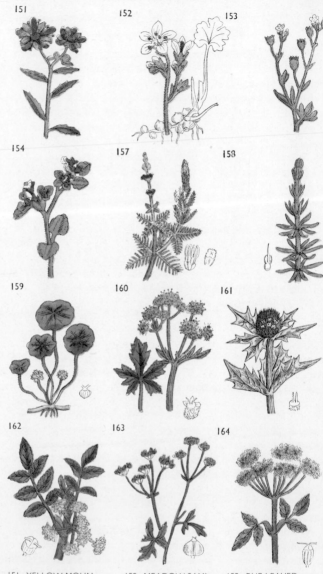

151. YELLOW MOUN-
    TAIN SAXIFRAGE.
154. GOLDEN SAXIFRAGE.
159. MARSH PENNYWORT.
162. MARSH-WORT.

152. MEADOW SAXI-
    FRAGE.
157. WATER MILFOIL.
160. WOOD SANICLE.
163. HEDGE SISON.

153. RUE-LEAVED
    SAXIFRAGE.
158. MARE'S-TAIL.
161. SEA HOLLY.
164. GOUTWEED.

UMBELLATE FAMILY: *Umbelliferae*

A large family with some 2,700 species which are most densely distributed in W. Asia and the Mediterranean regions. Contains both very poisonous and valuable food plants. Many are aromatic.

In Britain herbs, the small flowers with five petals being arranged in simple or compound umbels (see page 8). The leaves, often finely divided, are alternate, their stalks usually widened into a sheath at the base, though without proper stipules. The stems frequently hollow and jointed. The fruit is in two one-seeded parts of a typical structure. It often contains aromatic oils in special ducts. Although usually easy to identify the family, the genera are often difficult to separate. A close examination of the fruit, which is usually shown in the figures, is the best method.

Alexanders (*Smýrnium Olusátrum*), once cultivated for its young shoots which were boiled, is a biennial having a strong, round, and grooved stem up to 4 ft. high carrying dense, round, compound umbels of greenish-yellow flowers. Of meadows and waste land near the sea, and around gardens; only truly native in the S.

159. MARSH PENNYWORT, WHITE-ROT, *Hydrocótyle vulgáris, common.* Summer.

A small perennial, with its stem creeping along the mud, rooting at each joint. The flowers are minute, greenish-white. Of bogs, marshes, and water-sides. Name from Greek *hudor*, water, and *kotule*, cup, alluding to its situation and leaf-shape.

160. WOOD SANICLE, *Sanícula europaéa, European.* Summer.

Perennial, with stems about 1½ ft. high growing from a creeping rootstock. The inflorescence, although not very obviously, is a compound umbel. The fruit are hooked to help in their distribution. The name is from Latin *sano*, to heal.

161. SEA HOLLY, ERYNGO, *Erýngium marítimum, belonging to the sea.* Late summer.

A stiff plant, much branched, spreading by suckers, and of a bluish-grey colour. It has much the appearance of a teasel, and close examination of the inflorescence is required to see its umbelliferous nature. The blue colour of the flower is singular among British umbellifers.

162. MARSH-WORT, *Ápium nodiflórum, with flowers at the nodes*. Summer.

A creeping perennial, the flowering stems and leaves variable in size according to situation. Of marshy fields and ditches.

Celery has been evolved from wild celery (*A. graveólens, strong-smelling*) found occasionally in marshes and ditches near the sea. The wild plant is coarse, bitter, and, it is said, poisonous. It should not be mistaken for watercress (No. 30).

163. HEDGE SISON, HEDGE STONEWORT, BASTARD STONE PARSLEY, *Síson Amómum*. Summer.

Annual or biennial, from 2 ft. to 3 ft. high, freely branched in the upper part, with small and few flowers. In hedgerows and banks in S. England, less common elsewhere. The plant has a pungent smell.

164. GOUTWEED, BISHOPWEED, HERB GERARD, ASHWEED, GROUND ELDER, *Aegopódium Podragária*. Summer.

A coarse perennial with grooved stems up to 2 ft. high. The white creeping rootstock is aromatic and pungent to the taste. Found particularly in waste places near houses, having been cultivated in the past medicinally; it is probably not a true native. *Aegopódium*, from Greek, means goat's-foot.

165. CORN PARSLEY, *Cárum ségetum, of cornfields*. Summer to early autumn.

An erect slender annual, much branched, up to 2 ft. high. Found by roadsides and in waste places in the southern half of England.

Garden parsley is *C. Petroselinum*, from the Mediterranean, and is naturalized in places. Caraway, *C. Cárvi*, of which the aromatic carpels form caraway 'seeds,' is also found naturalized.

166. WATER-PARSNIP, *Síum latifólium, broad-leaved*. Summer.

Perennial with a creeping rootstock which sends up strong furrowed stems about 4 ft. high. The lesser water-parsnip (*S. erectum*) is smaller in its growth, more branched and leafy. Both are of ditches and wet places; the latter more widely spread, though both become scarce in the north. Both are reputed poisonous.

167. BURNET-SAXIFRAGE, *Pimpinélla Saxifraga*. Summer to autumn.

A perennial with a slender, slightly branching, and furrowed stem about 2 ft. high. Flowers sometimes pink. Of dry fields and banks.

168. HARE's ⁄ EAR, THOROW ⁄ WAX, *Bupleúrum rotundifólium, round ⁄ leaved.* Summer.

An erect smooth annual, about a foot high. With its undivided rounded leaves through which the stem passes, the plant is very un⁄ typical of the family. The flowers have leafy bracts that at first sight appear to be the petals; actually they surround the minute complete flowers. Of fields and downs in the S. and E. Called locally buplevers. An old name derived from Greek words meaning ox⁄rib.

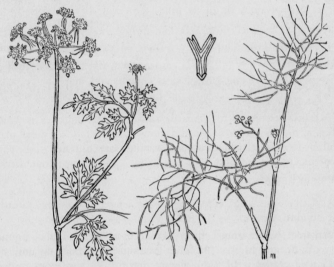

171. FOOL'S PARSLEY   172. FENNEL

169. WATER DROPWORT, *Oenánthe fistulósa, hollow.* Summer to autumn.

A perennial with tuberous creeping runners. The stems are swollen and hollow, about 3 ft. high. Of ditches, marshes, wet fields, etc. Common except in N. Scotland. No connection with dropwort (No. 360).

170. PARSLEY DROPWORT, *Oenánthe Lachenálii.* Summer to autumn.

Perennial, usually not so tall, and with more finely divided leaves than the above. Nor are the roots so tuberous. Hemlock dropwort (*O. crocáta, saffron⁄coloured*) is found by ditches and stream⁄sides. The root consists of several tubers, and the leaves are pinnate with segments larger than in the other kinds. The plant contains a juice which turns yellow when exposed to the air. It (and the other species) are poisonous; when cleared from ditches it may be eaten by stock with rapid fatal results.

171. FOOL'S PARSLEY, *Aethúsa Cynápium.* Summer to autumn.

An annual up to 2 ft. high. Smells unpleasantly when rubbed. Flowers white. A common weed of cultivation. It should be con-sidered as poisonous in all its parts (Text Fig. 171). Name from Greek *aitho,* to burn, on account of its reputed qualities.

172. FENNEL, *Foeniculum vulgáre, common.* Late summer to autumn.

Perennial up to 3 ft. or taller in gardens, with very fine leaf segments. Flowers yellow. Long cultivated as a herb, and may not be truly native. Usually near gardens, but found on rocky coasts except in the N. Used for a sauce. An oil is obtained from the seed (Text Fig. 172).

173. SAMPHIRE, *Críthmum marítimum, of the sea.* Summer.

A smooth perennial, about a foot high, the plant, including leaves and umbels, somewhat succulent. Of rocky places by the sea, rare in the N.

174. WILD ANGELICA, *Angélica sylvéstris, wild.* End of summer.

Perennial, with a stout hollow purplish stem from 2 ft. to, occasion-ally, 5 ft. or more high. The lower leaves are large, as are the umbels. Fruit flat, winged. Of damp woods, stream-sides, and moist places. The garden angelica, *Archangélica officinális, of use to man,* the stems of which are preserved and used for confectionery, is a European plant.

175. WILD PARSNIP, *Pastináca satíva, cultivated.* Summer.

An annual or biennial, forming a tap-root. Stems stout and fur-rowed, 2 ft. or more high according to situation. Fruit flat. Of wastes, field-sides, and banks. The origin of the cultivated parsnip, and, as such, often found as an escape from gardens.

176. COW-PARSNIP, HOGWEED, *Herácleum Sphondýlium.* Summer to autumn.

A coarse perennial, which may reach 5 ft. or more. The whole

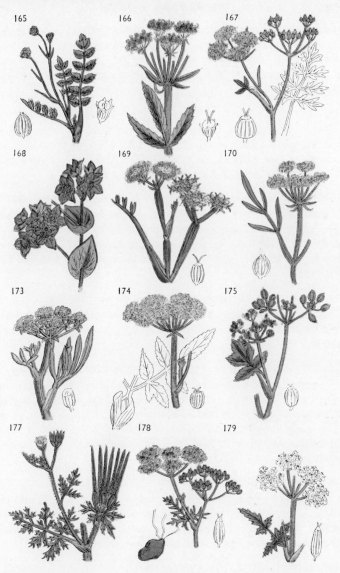

165. CORN PARSLEY.
168. HARE'S-EAR.
173. SAMPHIRE.
177. SHEPHERD'S
     NEEDLE.

166. WATER-PARSNIP.
169. WATER DROP-
     WORT.
174. WILD ANGELICA.
178. PIGNUT.

167. BURNET-SAXI-
     FRAGE.
170. PARSLEY DROP-
     WORT.
175. WILD PARSNIP.
179. WILD CHERVIL.

plant rough with short hairs. Flower white; the nectar is exposed on
a small disk at its centre, which is very attractive to small flies and beetles.
William Cobbett was one of those who advocated the parsnip-like
root as food for stock. Particularly common in hedgerows, field-sides,
and waste land (Text Fig. 176). Name derived from the god Hercules,
alluding to its strength.

176. COW-PARSNIP   181. WILD CARROT

177. SHEPHERD'S NEEDLE, VENUS'S COMB, *Scándix Pécten-Véneris.*
Summer.

An annual weed of cornfields, from 6 in. to 1 ft. high, of branching
growth and hairy. The beaked fruit, about 2 in. long, gives the plant
both its names. Not common in the N.

178. PIGNUT, EARTHNUT, *Conopódium denudátum, naked.* Summer.

A perennial, sending up slender stems from an underground
tuberous rootstock, roundish in shape — the 'nut' — which is edible.
Leaves delicately cut. Grows among grass in woods and fields.

179. WILD CHERVIL, COW PARSLEY, *Chaerophýllum sylvéstre, wild.*
Spring.

A perennial with a hairy branching stem up to 3 ft. high. Fruit smooth and without a beak. A very common hedgerow plant. Burr chervil (*C. Anthríscus*) is an annual, smaller and with more finely cut leaves than the last, and easily distinguished by its fruits, which are covered with short, hooked bristles, and have short beaks. Rough chervil (*C. temulum, nodding*) has purple-spotted stems up to 3 ft. high. Garden chervil (*C. Cerefólium*) comes from S.-E. Europe, and is found as an escape from cultivation.

180. HEDGE PARSLEY, *Caúcalis Anthríscus*. Summer to autumn.

An annual, with solid, wiry stems up to 3 ft. high. The whole plant is thinly covered with stiff hairs. Flowers white or pink. Of hedgerows, roadsides, and waste places.

181. WILD CARROT, BIRD'S-NEST, *Daúcus Caróta*. Summer and autumn.

Annual or biennial, stems from 1 ft. to 3ft. high, hairy. Bracts on umbels prominent and divided into from three to seven lobes. Flowers white or with a purple tinge. Of hedgerows, road- and field-sides. After flowering, the stalks of the umbels curve inwards, forming the 'bird's nest.' A form of the cultivated carrot, with a similar though much thinner root (Text Fig. 181).

182. HEMLOCK, *Coníum maculátum, spotted*. Summer.

A biennial with a hollow stem from 3 ft. to 5 ft. or more high which is marked with purplish dots. Fruit with crinkled edges. The plant smells unpleasantly mousy when bruised. Of waysides, banks, hedge-rows, waste places, and along streams. The leaves when fresh, the roots, and the fruit are all poisonous. Dried in hay it is harmless.

ARALIA FAMILY: *Araliáceae*

For the most part a tropical family closely allied in structure to the *Umbelliferae*.

Usually woody plants, with white or greenish-yellow flowers in umbels. Fruit, berry-like.

The 'aralia' of gardens is usually *Fátsia japónica, Japanese*, a member of this family. It bears 'about the biggest leaves of any hardy evergreen' —W. J. Bean. The Chinese angelica-tree sometimes found in gardens is, however, a true *Arália, A. chinénsis, Chinese*.

183. IVY, *Hédera Hélix*. Autumn.

An evergreen perennial, climbing high by means of root-like growths or scrambling along the ground. The flowers are never on these climbing or running shoots, but on bush-like growths, which usually occur when the plant has reached the top of its support. The berries are shiny black when ripe. Normally, of woodlands. It is a very variable plant, practically every kind cultivated being a variety of *H. Hélix*. It does little if any harm to the trees up which it climbs; nor does it damage buildings. The leaves are eaten and enjoyed by stock. 'Tree ivies' are cuttings from the bushy flowering parts; they seldom revert to the climbing form.

MISTLETOE FAMILY: *Lorantháceae*

For the most part shrubby evergreens, parasitic on the boughs of trees, mostly found in the tropics. Limited in Britain to the following:

184. MISTLETOE, *Viscum álbum, white*. Spring.

An evergreen shrub, yellowish-green in colour, with the male and female flowers on separate plants, parasitic on tree branches. Fruit a berry. Native in S. England, where it is most frequently found on apple-trees. Although it *will* grow on almost any kind of tree, it is seldom found on its traditional host, the oak. The sticky seeds are spread by birds wiping their beaks clean on branches after eating the fruit.

CORNEL OR DOGWOOD FAMILY: *Cornáceae*

Usually trees or shrubs, although some are herbs, of the N. hemisphere.

Leaves generally undivided and opposite, without stipules. Flowers small, in umbels. Fruit berry-like.

The 'variegated laurel' of shrubberies is a member of the family, a yellow-spotted form of *Aúcuba japónica, Japanese*, brought from Japan in 1783. This form is always female, and to produce the handsome red berries a plant of the green-leaved male must be placed near.

185. DOGWOOD, *Córnus sanguínea, blood-red*. Early summer.

A deciduous shrub about 6 ft. high. Flowers with a heavy scent. Ripe fruit black. Twigs blood-red in autumn. Of damp thickets and hedgerows in the S. Dogwood is a corruption of *dagwood*, the stems having been used for 'dags' or skewers. Dwarf cornel (*C. suéica, Swedish*) is a creeping perennial with stem about 6 in. high bearing stalkless egg-shaped leaves. The flowers, in summer, are minute, purple, surrounded by four large white bracts. On alpine moors in Scotland and the N. The cornelian cherry (*C. Mas*), an early-flowering small tree with yellow flowers opening before the leaves, native of Europe, has been cultivated in Britain for several centuries. Name from Latin *cornu*, a horn, referring to the hard wood.

HONEYSUCKLE FAMILY: *Caprifoliáceae*

A family of herbs, shrubs, and trees found principally in the N. temperate regions and on tropical mountains.

Leaves opposite without stipules. Flowers usually in heads, corymbs, or panicles. Perianth in one piece dividing into five (sometimes four) lobes. Fruit usually fleshy and berry-like.

The snowberry (*Symphoricárpus*) from N. America, *Leycestéria formósa, handsome*, from the Himalayas, and *Diervílla* (called weigela) from Japan, are well known in shrubberies.

186. MOSCHATEL, TOWN-CLOCK, *Adóxa Moschatellína*. Spring.

A perennial with a scaly rootstock which emits half-buried creeping runners. Stems square, brittle, up to 6 in. high. Of moist and shady places. Berry green. The name *Adoxa* is from the Greek, and refers to its insignificant appearance. It smells of musk, from which word 'moschatel' is derived.

187. COMMON ELDER, *Sambúcus nígra, black*. Early summer.

A deciduous shrub or small tree, with a rough, crooked stem. The flowers are scented, white or cream-coloured. It seeds itself freely in hedgerows, woods, and shady damp places. Once of great repute medicinally. Elderberry wine, made from the berries, is an old specific for colds and chills. Infusions of the flowers and leaves were also popular.

Dwarf elder, Danewort or Dane's blood (*S. Ébulus*), is traditionally said to have been brought to us by the Danes. It is a perennial herb up to 3 ft. high with pinnately compound leaves. Flowers white or purplish in smaller corymbs than *S. nígra*; fruits black, poisonous. Of shady waste places. Name from Greek *sambuke*, a musical instrument made from the wood.

188. WAYFARING TREE, MEAL TREE, *Vibúrnum Lantána*. Early summer.

A large deciduous shrub, up to 15 ft. high. The young shoots and leaves, and the undersides of the old leaves, covered with a mealy down.

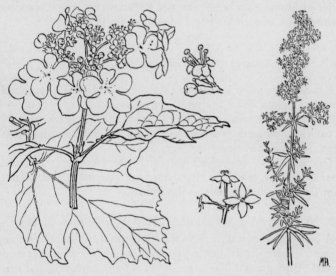

189. GUELDER ROSE   193. LADY'S BEDSTRAW

Fruit oblong, about ⅓ in. long, red becoming black. Of woods and hedgerows, more particularly in the S.

189. GUELDER ROSE, *Vibúrnum Ópulus*. Summer.

A deciduous shrub, of 10 ft. or more, with grey stems. The flower has an outer ring of sterile, showy white flowers which surrounds a centre composed of smaller fertile flowers. In the garden guelder rose (*V. Ópulus* var. *stérile*) the inflorescence is larger and showier because it consists entirely of sterile flowers (as does that of the conservatory hydrangea). As a result, the gardener misses the beautiful red fruits which cover the wild plants in autumn (Text Fig. 189).

The laurustinus (*V. Tínus*) is a dense evergreen shrub with white flowers in winter and early spring, native of the Mediterranean district, and grown in Britain since the sixteenth century. Recently, many Chinese viburnums, some very hardy and flowering in late winter, have been introduced.

190. WOODBINE, HONEYSUCKLE, *Lonícera Periclýmenum*. Summer to autumn.

A deciduous shrub, with twining stems up to 20 ft. long, which climb over bushes and trees. The flowers are sweetly scented, and are followed by small red berries. Of woods, thickets, and hedges. Several kinds of honeysuckle are cultivated, including both climbing and shrubby forms. They come from Europe, Asia, and N. America. Named after Lonitzer, a sixteenth‑century German physician and botanist.

BEDSTRAW FAMILY: *Rubiáceae*

One of the most extensive families of tropical plants, with some 5,500 species—a few of which are found, however, in the Arctic.

In Britain, all are herbs with usually narrow undivided leaves, arranged in whorls. Stems angular, often covered with rough hairs. Flowers small, calyx usually missing, the corolla being in one piece dividing into four or five spreading lobes.

It includes several important economic plants, such as coffee (*Cóffea*) cultivated in S. Brazil and elsewhere; *Cinchóna*, trees from the Andes whose bark yields quinine; and *Uragóga Ipecacuánha* from Brazil whose root yields the drug ipecacuanah.

191. WILD MADDER, *Rúbia peregrína, foreign*. Summer.

A straggling evergreen perennial with long stems sometimes trailing over bushes, holding by the prickles on it and the leaves. Fruit a small black berry either in one or two lobes. Of dry woods and stony places, usually near the S.‑W. coasts. Dyer's madder (*R. tinctória, used for dyeing*) is very similar, and was once cultivated in S. Europe for the dye alizarin crimson, now produced synthetically. The name from the Latin *ruber*, red, refers to this colouring.

192. CROSSWORT, *Gálium Cruciáta*. Spring to early summer.

Perennial, branching at the base into short, weak, leafy stems and erect

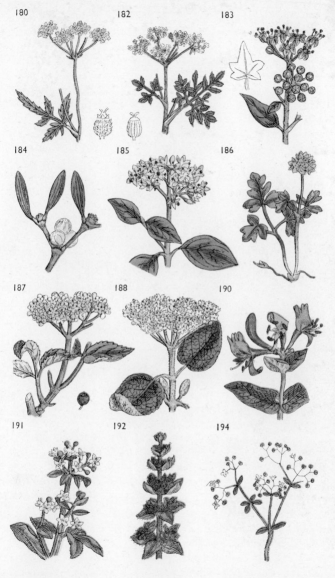

180. HEDGE PARSLEY.
184. MISTLETOE.
187. COMMON ELDER.
191. WILD MADDER.

182. HEMLOCK.
185. DOGWOOD.
188. WAYFARING
        TREE.
192. CROSSWORT.

183. IVY.
186. MOSCHATEL.
190. WOODBINE.
194. WATER BED-
        STRAW.

flowering stems, a foot or so high. Of hedgerows and copses. A number of the flowers are male, and fall early.

193. LADY'S BEDSTRAW, *Gálium vérum, true.* Summer.

Perennial, branching into many fine stems, spreading or erect, about a foot high, ending in panicles of minute yellow, sweetly scented flowers. Of banks, dry pastures, and downs. It was once used to curdle milk in cheese-making, and in places is still called cheese-rennet. It was used also as a dye (Text Fig. 193).

194. WATER BEDSTRAW, *Gálium palústre, of marshes.* Summer.

Perennial, with creeping rootstock, and weak stems bearing the leaves usually in whorls of four. The bog bedstraw (*G. uliginósum, of swamps*) is rather similar, but with narrower sharply pointed leaves arranged in whorls of six to eight.

195. STONE OR HEATH BEDSTRAW, *Gálium saxátile, of rocks.* Summer.

A small, tufted perennial, with numerous weak trailing flowering stems. Leaves pointed, usually six in a whorl. Of heaths and upland fields.

196. HEDGE BEDSTRAW, *Gálium Mollúgo.* Summer.

Perennial with straggling square stems 3 ft. or more long, hairy on the angles but without prickles. Leaves usually eight in a whorl. Fruit without hooks. Found scrambling in hedgerows and thickets, common except in N. Scotland.

197. GOOSE-GRASS, CLEAVERS, *Gálium Aparíne.* Summer to autumn.

A vigorous annual, the trailing stems 3 ft. or more long, clinging to hedges and banks by small curved prickles on their four ridges, as well as the edges and midribs of the leaves (which are in whorls of six to eight). The fruit is covered with hooks, which catch on the fur of animals and help in its distribution. Name from Latin *gala*, milk, from the use of No. 193.

198. WOODRUFF, *Aspérula odoráta, scented.* Spring to early summer.

A perennial with a creeping rootstock. Stems erect, about 9 in. high. The leaves arranged in whorls, usually of eight, give the

G

appearance of a series of ruffs. Of woods and shady places. When drying, gives off a scent of new-mown hay. Formerly used to scent linen, etc.

199. SQUINANCYWORT, *Aspérula cyánchica, of quinsy.* Summer.

A perennial, somewhat similar to the above, but smaller. Leaves in fours or twos. Scentless when dried. Of dry, limy soils, most frequently in the S. A remedy for squinancy, now called quinsy. Name from Latin *asper*, rough, a quality of certain exotic kinds.

200. FIELD MADDER, *Sherárdia arvénsis, of cultivated fields.* Spring to autumn.

An annual, about 6 in. high, branching at the base, the stems lying along the ground. Leaves usually in sixes. Flowers blue or pink. Usually a weed of cultivation. Named after W. Sherard (1659–1728) who founded the chair of botany at Oxford University.

VALERIAN FAMILY: *Valerianáceae*

A cosmopolitan family of herbs, in Britain annual or perennial, with opposite leaves, without stipules. Calyx a small ring, often almost imperceptible at the time of flowering, but later becoming feathery and surmounting the seeds. Corolla tubular at the base, with a spur, dividing usually into five spreading lobes. Flowers in a terminal corymb or panicle.

The red valerian of gardens is a Mediterranean plant, *Centránthus rúber, red.*

201. VALERIAN, ALL-HEAL, *Valeriána officinális, of use to man.* Summer.

A perennial, spreading by suckers, from 2 ft. to 4 ft. or more high. Flowers vary from white to pink. Of moist woods and fields. Once a famous drug for innumerable complaints. To-day a preparation from the rootstock with stimulative properties is used for hysteria and nervous troubles, and palpitation of the heart.

202. LAMB'S LETTUCE, CORNSALAD, *Valerianélla olitória, of domestic use.* Spring to early summer.

An annual up to 1 ft. high. Stem juicy and repeatedly forked.

Flowers very small and surrounded by green bracts. Of hedgerows, fields, and waste places. Introduced from S. Europe as a plant cultivated for salad. *Valerianella* is the diminutive of *Valeriana*.

TEASEL FAMILY: *Dipsáceae*

A small family, mostly N. temperate in distribution.

In Britain, herbs with opposite leaves, without stipules. The flowers or florets, which have a tubular corolla divided into four or five petal-like lobes, are collected into domed heads.

The head is protected by a ring of bracts, and the calyx of each floret is contained in what appears to be an outer calyx but which is really formed from *bracteoles* or small bracts. The structure of these flower-heads is somewhat similar to those of the daisy family, which has, however, no proper calyx to its florets. Further, the anthers of the daisies are joined in a tube, while in the teasels they are free.

203. WILD TEASEL, *Dípsacus sylvéstris, wild*. Late summer to autumn.

Biennial, producing a tuft of radical leaves only the first year and a strong, ribbed flower-stem, up to 5 ft. high, the second. The whole plant is prickly. The bracts of the florets harden into spines. Of waste places. The fuller's teasel (*D. fullónum, used for carding wool*) has hooked bracts, and is used for raising the nap on cloth. The large bracts surrounding the flower-heads form a cup which collects water; the name from the Greek *dipso*, I thirst, is said to allude to this.

204. DEVIL'S-BIT, *Scabiósa succisa, cut-off*. Summer to autumn.

A perennial from 1 ft. to 2 ft. high. Radical leaves entire, hairy; upper generally toothed. Corolla four-lobed. The rootstock has the appearance of having had its end cut off. Of fields, heaths, and open woodland.

205. SMALL SCABIOUS, *Scabiósa Columbária*. Summer to autumn.

A perennial, radical leaves undivided. Not usually as tall as the last. The stem leaves deeply cut. Corolla five-lobed. Of pastures and waste places, particularly on limy soils.

206. FIELD SCABIOUS, *Scabiósa arvénsis, of cultivated fields*. Summer.

Perennial, sometimes 3 ft. high. Stems branched, and with the leaves hairy. The leaves are elliptical and lobed, the upper more deeply so. Of pastures, open woodland, cultivated and waste land. *Scabiosa* is derived from the Latin *scabies*, the itch, for which it was once used as a remedy.

COMPOSITE or DAISY FAMILY: *Compósitae*

This is the largest family. With some 13,000 species, distributed all over the world in every kind of situation, it includes about one-tenth of the world's flowering plants. Among its members are huge cactus-like succulents growing in deserts, such herbaceous plants as the little daisy of meadows, and minute daisy-like plants growing on the highest and coldest mountains.

The family is distinguished by its flowers, or florets, being arranged in a distinctive head (see page 8 and Plate II). They are most usually yellow, white, or purple, and the fruit (nut-like) is often attached to a stalk which carries a downy tuft, which is caught and blown about by the wind.

The family is decorative rather than useful to man; the Jerusalem artichoke (*Heliánthus tuberósus, tuberous*), which owes its name not to a place but to the corruption of the old name for helianthus, *girasol* (turn-to-the-sun), grown for its edible tubers; the globe artichoke (*Cýnara Scolýmus*), grown for its edible flower-heads; the less common cardoon (*Cýnara Cardúnculus*), for its stems; and lettuce, cultivated forms of *Lactúca* whose origin is obscure, are usually the only composites in the kitchen garden.

On the other hand, the *Dáhlia* from Mexico, the *Zínnia* from Mexico, the French and African marigolds (*Tágetes*) from Peru, the marigold (*Caléndula*) from S. Europe, and the everlasting flowers (*Helichrýsum, Acroclínium*, and other genera) from S. Africa, are only a few of the exotic composites which have been developed by the gardener.

To balance this, the order provides us with such pernicious weeds as the ragwort, thistles, dandelion, and groundsel.

207. HEMP AGRIMONY, *Eupatórium cannabínum, hemp-like*. Summer.

Perennial with erect stems 3 ft. or more high. Leaves opposite, and usually cut into coarsely toothed lobes. Of thickets and water-side banks. Both flower-heads and leaves appear untypical of the family. The plant bears a superficial likeness to hemp (*Cánnabis*).

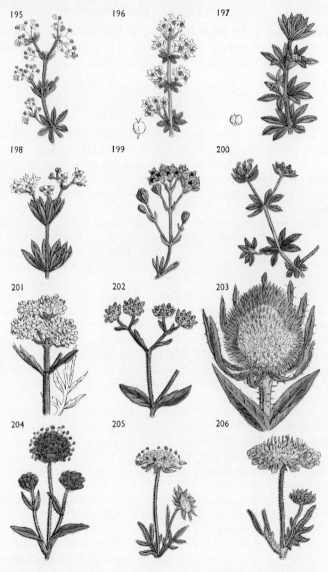

195. STONE BED-
      STRAW.
198. WOODRUFF.
201. VALERIAN.
204. DEVIL'S-BIT.

196. HEDGE BED-
      STRAW.
199. SQUINANCYWORT.
202. LAMB'S LETTUCE.
205. SMALL SCABIOUS.

197. GOOSE-GRASS.
200. FIELD MADDER.
203. WILD TEASEL.
206. FIELD SCABIOUS.

208. GOLDEN ROD, *Solidágo Virgaúrea.* Summer to autumn.

Perennial with stems up to 2 ft. high. Stem leaves narrow without stalks, and generally slightly toothed. Leaves at base broader and stalked. Larger introduced kinds are grown in gardens, and are often found naturalized near them.

209. DAISY, *Béllis perénnis.* Most of the year.

A tufted perennial up to 6 in. high. The leaves are spoon-shaped; cutting them off causes the plant to branch and spread. Flower, ray

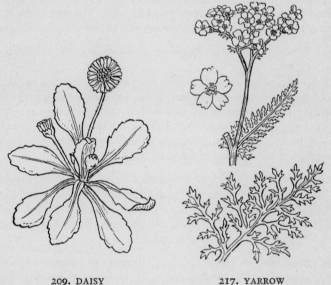

209. DAISY   217. YARROW

white, sometimes tinged with red; disk golden. Common in all grass-land (Text Fig. 209).

210. SEA STARWORT, SEA ASTER, *Áster Tripólium.* Late summer to autumn.

A perennial, slightly branching. Leaves narrow and fleshy. Of salt-marshes. The modern garden michaelmas daisy is a hybrid aster; two of its most important ancestors came from the U.S.A. The China aster does not belong to this genus, but to *Callistéma,* from E. Africa. *Aster* is the Latin for star—the inflorescences being star-like.

211. BLUE FLEABANE, *Erígeron ácris, sharp*. Summer to autumn.

An annual or biennial up to 1 ft. high. Stem erect, slightly branched and reddish-coloured. Leaves narrow and entire. Of dry places, especially on chalk. The garden erigerons are from N. America. *Erigeron* is from the Greek, meaning literally 'early hoar,' referring to the down on the fruit.

212. CAT'S-EAR, CAT'S-FOOT, MOUNTAIN EVERLASTING, *Antén-naria dioíca, dioecius*. Early summer.

A creeping or low, tufted perennial an inch or two high. Leaves often whitish. Of mountain pastures and heaths. The tufts on the male flower have been likened to the *antennae* of a butterfly, hence the name.

213. WOOD CUDWEED, *Gnaphálium sylváticum, of woods*. Summer to autumn.

Perennial, tufted at the base with flowering stems up to 8 in. high. Basal leaves lance-shaped on long stalks; on stem, narrow, and often cottony. Marsh cudweed (*G. uliginósum, of marshes*) is an annual, some 6 in. high, with narrow, wavy, and cottony leaves. The brownish flower-heads are clustered among the upper leaves. Name from Greek *gnaphalion*, wool, referring to the hairy leaves.

214. PLOUGHMAN'S SPIKENARD, *Ínula Conýza*. Summer to autumn.

An erect biennial up to 3 ft. high, with down on leaves and stem. The lower leaves are broadly lance-shaped, on stalks; the stem leaves stalkless. Of dry places, copses, and waysides, particularly on limy soils. Not found in Scotland or Ireland.

215. ELECAMPANE, *Ínula Helénium*. Summer to autumn.

A coarse, branching perennial, 2 ft. or more high. The basal leaves are long, narrowing into a stalk, while the upper leaves clasp the stem. Once widely planted as an antiseptic aromatic herb, the root being candied and used for chest troubles. An ingredient of absinthe. Generally found near old gardens, naturalized. Common fleabane (*I. dysenterica, of dysentry*) is a woolly perennial with arrow-shaped leaves clasping the stem, and yellow flowers. Of wet places, rare in the N.

216. THREE-CLEFT BUR-MARIGOLD, *Bídens tripartíta, three-parted*. Summer to autumn.

An annual, from 1 ft. to 3 ft. high, with a branching stem. The

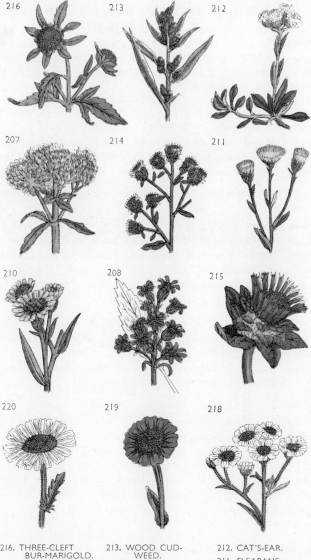

216. THREE-CLEFT
    BUR-MARIGOLD.
207. HEMP AGRIMONY.
210. SEA STARWORT.
220. OX-EYE OR DOG-
    DAISY.

213. WOOD CUD-
    WEED.
214. PLOUGHMAN'S
    SPIKENARD.
208. GOLDEN ROD.
219. CORN MARIGOLD.

212. CAT'S-EAR.

211. FLEABANE.

215. ELECAMPANE.

218. SNEEZEWORT.

leaves are cut into three or five segments. Of ditches and marshes. Bur-marigold (*B. cérnua, drooping*) is very similar but with undivided leaves. Both become uncommon in N. Scotland. *Bidens*, from the Latin, with two teeth, refers to two stiff bristles found on the fruit.

217. MILFOIL, YARROW, *Achilléa Millefólium*. Summer onwards.

A perennial with a creeping underground rootstock which sends up short leafy stems and erect flowering stems up to 1½ ft. high. The ray florets are white or pink, the disk golden. Sometimes the whole plant is woolly. Almost universal in fields and waste places (Text Fig. 217).

218. SNEEZEWORT, GOOSEWORT, *Achilléa Ptármica*. Late summer onwards.

A perennial with creeping rootstock. Stems up to 2 ft. high. Leaves undivided and serrated. Flower-heads few. Of pastures and moist places.

The genus was dedicated to Achilles, who, legend says, used it to staunch his wounds, a purpose for which the British species were regularly used.

219. CORN MARIGOLD, *Chrysánthemum ségetum, of cornfields*. Summer.

An annual up to 1½ ft. high, with somewhat fleshy and aromatic leaves. Frequent as a weed in cornfields.

220. OX-EYE or DOG-DAISY, *Chrysánthemum Leucánthemum*. Late spring to summer.

Perennial, stem slightly branched, up to 2 ft. high. Leaves at base stalked and coarsely toothed. Of meadows, banks, etc. The autumn-flowering florists and garden chrysanthemums have been evolved from Asiatic species, particularly *C. sinense, Chinese*, and *C. índicum, Indian*. They have been cultivated here for about a century. The garden pyrethrum and marguerite are among other exotic species introduced from Europe and Asia.

Chrysanthemum, from the Greek, means 'gold-flower.'

221. SCENTLESS MAYWEED, *Matricária inodóra, scentless*. Spring onwards.

A branching annual up to 1½ ft. high, with finely divided leaves. These, and the flower, are scentless. Flower, ray white, disk yellow

(Text Fig. 221). The wild or false chamomile (*M. Chamomílla*) is rather similar to the last; the flowers are smaller (about ¾ in. diameter) arranged in a corymb, and when touched the leaves smell sweetly of chamomile. Both are found in fields and waste places.

222. WILD CHAMOMILE, STINKING MAYWEED, *Ánthemis Cótula.* Summer to autumn.

A branching annual, 1 ft. or so high. Flowers in a terminal corymb. Rather similar to the above, but easily distinguished by its unpleasant

221. SCENTLESS MAYWEED   234. CREEPING THISTLE

smell when touched. A weed of cultivated ground and waste places, uncommon in the N.

223. CORN CHAMOMILE, *Ánthemis arvénsis, of cultivated fields.* Spring to summer.

Annual or biennial up to 1½ ft. high, coarser than the above and usually downy, with single flower-heads. The disk is flat. The stem is much branched, and somewhat decumbent. A weed of cultivation, uncommon in the N. and Scotland. The true chamomile (*A. nóbilis, noble*) is an aromatic plant, native in the S., but usually found as an escape from cultivation. It was much grown for use as a stomachic.

224. TANSY, *Tanacétum vulgáris, common.* Late summer and autumn.

An erect perennial up to 3 ft. high, spreading by suckers. The whole plant has a heavy aromatic smell, and a bitter taste. It was once much used as a flavouring as well as a medicine of varied purposes. Usually found near gardens.

225. MUGWORT, *Artemísia vulgáris, common.* Late summer to autumn.

An aromatic perennial with rough, red stems about 3 ft. high. Of hedgerows, roadsides, and waste places. Once used to give a bitter flavour to drinks; wormwood (*A. Absínthium*), sometimes found near the sea, is still used in the making of absinthe.

226. COLTSFOOT, *Tussilágo Fárfara.* Early spring onwards.

A creeping perennial, with flowering stems about 6 in. high appearing before the leaves, which are broadly heart-shaped and toothed. The whole plant is covered with cottony down. Of waste land, and in damp, heavy soil a troublesome weed. Name from the Latin *tussis*, cough, for which it was a medicine.

227. BUTTERBUR, *Petasítes vulgáris, common.* Spring.

A creeping perennial, throwing up flowering stems about 1 ft. high before the leaves, which are very large, heart- or kidney-shaped with a toothed edge and hairy. The plants bear either preponderately male or female flower-heads. Of damp places such as stream- or road-sides. The winter heliotrope (*P. frágrans, fragrant*) is an introduced plant that is very similar, but has sweetly scented flowers in early spring. Found where naturalized; once planted in a suitable place it is difficult to eradicate, and becomes an overpowering weed. Name from Greek, *petasos*, a broad-brimmed hat, with reference to the leaves.

228. GROUNDSEL, *Senécio vulgáris, common.* Most of the year.

An erect branching annual, between 6 in. and 1 ft. high. The flowers are usually without a ray. One of the commonest weeds of cultivation. Contrary to tradition, it should not be given to cage birds; it contains a poison which is cumulative in its effects on the liver.

229. RAGWORT, RAGWEED, *Senécio Jacobaéa.* Summer to autumn.

A biennial or perennial with erect stems from 2 ft. to 4 ft. high. The leaves at the base are stalked. A widespread and dangerous weed of pastures and waste lands, containing a poison which is slow and cumulative in its effect on stock, and its regular consumption is particularly dangerous to cattle. Its destruction may be made compulsory by the local authority. Marsh ragwort (*S. aquáticus, of water*), found in wet places, is very similar to the last, but usually more branched and shorter. 'Rag' refers to the raggedly cut leaves. *Senécio* is from the Latin *senex*, old man, an allusion to the white down surmounting the calyx; it is a huge and widespread genus, with some 2,000 species; including giant desert succulents.

230. BURDOCK, *Árctium Láppa.* Summer to early autumn.

An erect branching biennial, usually 3 ft. to 4 ft. or more high. The lower heart-shaped leaves are thick and large. The bracts of the head end in hooks, which, when the fruit is ripe, catch on the coats of animals and are carried about. Variable in form, and often divided into two or more species. Once much used as an aperient and cure for rheumatism. Name from Greek *arktos*, a bear, an allusion to the coarse appearance of the plant.

231. SAW-WORT, *Serrátula tinctória, used for dyeing.* Late summer.

An erect perennial up to 3 ft. high. The lower leaves are stalked and deeply pinnately lobed. Of open woods and thickets. Once used as a yellow dye. Name from the Latin *serrula*, a saw, on account of the toothed leaves.

232. SPEAR or **PLUME THISTLE,** *Cárduus lanceolátus, lance-shaped.* Summer to autumn.

A strong biennial, 3 ft. to 4 ft. or more high, with a winged and prickly stem. Leaves narrow, wavy, and ending in a prickly point. Very common in fields, hedgerows, and waste places.

233. MARSH THISTLE, *Cárduus palústris, of marshes.* Summer to early autumn.

An erect annual or biennial up to 5 ft. high. The leaves are soft and hairy and continue for some distance down the stems as spiny wings. Of wet fields.

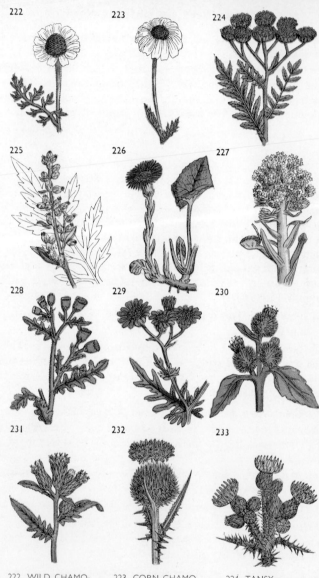

222. WILD CHAMO-
      MILE.
225. MUGWORT.
228. GROUNDSEL.
231. SAW-WORT.

223. CORN CHAMO-
      MILE.
226. BUTTERBUR.
229. RAGWORT.
232. SPEAR THISTLE.

224. TANSY.
227. COLTSFOOT.
230. BURDOCK.
233. MARSH THISTLE.

234. CREEPING THISTLE, *Cárduus arvénsis, of cultivated fields*. Late summer.

A perennial with a creeping rootstock, which makes it a difficult weed to eradicate. Stems from 2 ft. to 4 ft. high, angular. The male flowers in globular heads and the female in egg-shaped, are normally on separate plants. The florets are dull purple (Text Fig. 234).

235. MELANCHOLY or DARK PLUME THISTLE, *Cárduus heterophýllus, varied-leaved*. Summer.

Perennial with a creeping rootstock, stem stout and furrowed, from 2 ft. to 3 ft. high. It is not prickly. Leaves clasping the stem, white and cottony underneath. Of pastures in Scotland and the N. The dwarf thistle (*C. acaúlis, stemless*), flowering in late summer, almost stemless, of limy soils in the S.; the meadow thistle (*C. praténsis, of meadows*), about 2 ft. high, with rather tuberous roots and wavy leaves, of moist places in the S.; and the welted thistle (*C. crispus, curled*), spiny and cottony, with winged, branched stems 3 ft. or more high, and flowers nearly sessile in heads, are common. The Scotch thistle has been variously identified.

236. CARLINE THISTLE, *Carlína vulgáris, common*. Summer to autumn.

A biennial up to 1 ft. high. Leaves dense and very prickly; the outer bracts are edged with very prickly teeth. Of dry pastures among hills, and in sandy soils. Not common in Scotland. Named after the Emperor Charlemagne.

237. KNAPWEED, HARDHEADS, *Centauréa nígra, black*. Summer.

Perennial, from 1 ft. to 3 ft. with a grooved stem. Leaves green and rough with small hairs. The outer bracts of the head are fringed, and brownish-coloured. The dry, hard feel of the inflorescence gives a name to the plant. The florets are purple. Found almost universally in fields and grassy places (Text Fig. 237, inset a floret).

238. GREATER KNAPWEED, *Centauréa Scabiósa*. Summer to autumn.

Perennial of rather stronger growth than the last, and with pinnately divided leaves. The ray florets are showy, and are divided into five long lobes. Of similar situations to the above.

239. CORNFLOWER, BLUEBOTTLE, *Centauréa Cýanus*. Summer.

An erect annual, with a slender, downy stem, about 2 ft. high. Lower leaves usually lobed. A weed of cornfields.

Several kinds of *Centauréa* are grown in gardens, especially selected forms of the cornflower (including colours other than blue) and the sweet sultan (*C. moschàta, musk-scented*) from Persia. *Centauréa* should not be confused with centaury (No. 287).

240. GOAT'S-BEARD, JACK-GO-TO-BED-AT-NOON, *Tragopógon pra-ténsis, of meadows.* Early summer.

A biennial from 1 ft. to 2 ft. high, with rather grass-like leaves. Florets only open in the morning, hence its popular name. The fruit

237. KNAPWEED   243. AUTUMNAL HAWKBIT

has a 'beard' or tuft of down at the end of a long stalk or 'beak.' Of meadows and waste lands, usually where the soil is good. It has a thick tap-root and in salsify (*T. porrifólium, with leek-like leaves*), intro-duced from the Mediterranean regions, this is eaten. This plant is rather similar to the last, but has a purple flower. *Tragopógon*, from the Greek, means goat's-beard.

241. HAWKWEED PICRIS, *Pícris hieracioídes, Hieracium-like.* Summer to autumn.

A biennial with a stout branching stem, from 1 ft. to 2 ft. or more

235. MELANCHOLY THISTLE.
239. CORNFLOWER.
242. COMMON HAWKBIT.
246. CORN SOW-THISTLE.

236. CARLINE THISTLE.
240. GOAT'S-BEARD.
244. LESSER HAWK-BIT.
247. COMMON SOW-THISTLE.

238. GREATER KNAP-WEED.
241. HAWKWEED PICRIS.
245. CAT'S-EAR.
248. DANDELION.

high, covered with clinging hairs. The lower leaves are long and lance-shaped, tapering to a stalk. Of waysides and waste places, usually in dry situations. Name from Greek *picros*, bitter, alluding to the taste of the milky juice.

242. COMMON or ROUGH HAWKBIT, *Leóntodon híspidus, with bristly hairs.* Summer to autumn.

Perennial with long, narrow, spreading leaves at the base. The flower-heads are solitary on a stem 6 in. or more high. The whole plant is covered with stiff, short hairs. A typical pasture plant, except in N. Scotland.

243. AUTUMNAL HAWKBIT, *Leóntodon autumnális, of autumn.* Summer to autumn.

Perennial, with lower leaves long, narrow, and pinnately lobed. Flower-heads yellow, on branched stems about 1 ft. or more high. swollen and hollow below each head. Of fields and waste places (Text Fig. 243).

244. LESSER or HAIRY HAWKBIT, *Leóntodon hírtus, hairy.* Summer.

A perennial, about 6 in. high, usually rather sparsely covered with stiff hairs. Of dry fields, waste places, and commons. *Leontodon* is derived from the Greek words meaning 'lion's tooth,' referring to the toothed leaves.

245. CAT'S-EAR, *Hypochoéris radicáta, rooted.* Summer to autumn.

Perennial, with a thick and woody tap-root (to which the specific name refers), which sends up rough, spreading leaves. Flower-stem leafless, branched, from 1 ft. to 2 ft. high. Of fields and waste places.

246. CORN SOWTHISTLE, *Sónchus arvénsis, of cultivated fields.* Summer to autumn.

Perennial, with a creeping rootstock. Stems hollow, up to 3 ft. or more high. Lower leaves stalked, upper clasping the stem. A handsome weed of arable land and around cultivated places.

247. COMMON SOWTHISTLE, *Sónchus oleráceous, edible.* Early summer onwards.

An annual, somewhat similar to the last but smaller. Leaves clasp the stem with long ears.   One of the commonest weeds of cultivation, and spread to many parts of the world.

248. DANDELION, *Taráxacum officinále, of use to man.*   Early spring to
    late autumn.

Perennial with a long tap-root, black outside, from which spread the leaves in a rosette.   If the top of the plant and root is cut off, several buds are developed on the remaining root, and more rosettes grow.   Therefore, the whole root must be removed when weeding. The inflorescence is typical of one class of composites, being composed of ray-florets only, without any disk.   Each floret is perfect, with anthers and stigma.   Of grassland and as a weed of cultivation throughout the N. hemisphere to the Arctic.   The root was long used as a bitter aperient tonic, and the leaves, blanched, are good in salads.

249. SMOOTH HAWK'S-BEARD, *Crépis capilláris, hair-like.*   Summer.

An annual, the flower-stem branching, from 1 ft. to 3 ft. high.   The upper leaves clasp the stem with pointed ears.   Of fields, waysides, and dry banks.

250. MOUSE-EAR HAWKWEED, *Hierácium Pilosélla.*   Late spring and
    summer.

Perennial, with a tuft of leaves surrounded by leafy runners sent out from the rootstock.   Leaves covered with whitish down underneath. Flower-heads, often reddish outside, solitary on unbranched stems about 6 in. high.   Of dry fields and commons.

251. WALL HAWKWEED, *Hierácium murórum, of walls.*   Summer and
    early autumn.

Perennial, with a rosette of stalked leaves, from which rises an erect flower-stem from 1 ft. to 2 ft. high carrying several flower-heads in a terminal corymb.   Of banks, walls, fields, stony places, open woods, and shady places.   A variable plant.

252. NARROW-LEAVED HAWKWEED, *Hierácium umbellátum, umbellate.*
    Late summer to autumn.

A perennial with an erect leafy stem up to 3 ft. high, without, or with very few, leaves from the rootstock.   Flowers in an irregular umbel at the top of the stem, and at the axils of the leaves lower down.   Of

dry, stony places. *Hieracium* is derived from the Greek *hierax*, a hawk. It is a large genus, and some botanists have split it up into very many little-differentiated species. *Hierácium aurantíacum, orange-coloured,* from Europe, known as 'Grim-the-Collier,' often escapes from gardens, where it may become an annoying weed.

253. CHICORY, SUCCORY, *Cichórium Íntybus.* Summer to autumn.

A perennial with a tap-root and leaves rather similar in appearance to a dandelion, but easily differentiated by the flower-stem, which has a few lobed leaves which clasp it, and is about 2 ft. high, branched, bearing the flowers usually in pairs. Of waysides and in dry places on chalky soils, usually in the S.

The root was once widely used as a substitute for coffee; the leaves, blanched, are used for salads. Selected forms of endive (*C. Endívia*) from Asia are also grown for salad.

254. NIPPLEWORT, *Lápsana commúnis, common.* Summer to autumn.

A branching annual sometimes 3 ft. high but usually shorter. Leaves usually hairy, flower-heads small. Fruit without downy tuft. A common weed of cultivated and waste land (Text Fig. 254).

CAMPANULA FAMILY: *Campanuláceae*

A family of perennial herbs and also a few trees and shrubs, found mostly in the temperate parts of N. and S. hemispheres, and in the mountains of the tropics.

It consists of herbs having a milky juice. Leaves alternate, without stipules. The corolla is in one piece and is divided into five lobes. The five stamens are connected to the base of the corolla.

The flowers are often bell-shaped, usually blue or white in colour, and sometimes collected in heads. Fruit a capsule. The flowers are rather similar to the heath family, which consists, however, entirely of shrubs.

255. WATER LOBELIA, *Lobélia Dortmánna.* Summer.

An aquatic perennial, spreading by creeping runners. The leaves, almost cylindrical and consisting of two hollow tubes, carpet the bottom. Flower-stems rise about 6 in. out of the water. Of shallows in lakes in Scotland, Ireland, Wales, and N. England, but not found in the C., E., or S. Numerous lobelias are grown in gardens, particularly the dwarf bedding forms of *L. Erinus* from the Cape, introduced in 1752, and half-hardy species from N. and S. America. Named after the Fleming, Mathias de L'Obel, who was botanist to James I.

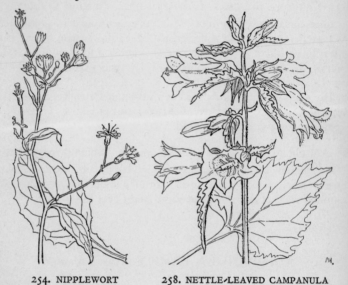

254. NIPPLEWORT   258. NETTLE-LEAVED CAMPANULA

256. SHEEP'S-BIT, SHEEP'S-SCABIOUS, *Jasíone montána*, *of mountains*. Summer.

Annual or biennial, with a rosette of stalked spoon-shaped leaves, and a branching, slender stem about 1 ft. high. Of dry, sandy soils, heaths, etc., more particularly in the S. No relative of the true scabious (Nos. 204–6) nor is it, as at first sight it may appear, a member of the daisy family.

257. CLUSTERED CAMPANULA, *Campánula glomeráta*, *with a rounded head of flowers*. Summer.

Biennial from 6 in. to 1½ ft. high, according to situation. Stem un-branched, hairy, clasped by its leaves, among the upper of which are the flowers. These are almost stalkless, in clusters. The radical leaves

249. SMOOTH HAWK'S-
BEARD.
252. NARROW-LEAVED
HAWKWEED.
256. SHEEP'S-BIT.
261. VENUS'S LOOK-
ING-GLASS.

250. MOUSE-EAR
HAWKWEED.
253. CHICORY.
257. CLUSTERED
CAMPANULA.
262. BILBERRY.

251. WALL HAWK-
WEED.
255. WATER LOBELIA.
260. IVY-LEAVED
BELLFLOWER.
263. COWBERRY.

are heart-shaped and stalked. Of dry fields, rare in the W. and Ireland, and only in the E. of Scotland. Selected forms are grown in gardens.

258. NETTLE-LEAVED CAMPANULA, *Campánula Trachélium.* Summer.

Biennial, the stem up to 3 ft. high. Radical leaves large, heart-shaped, and stalked. Stem leaves becoming more lance-shaped and stalkless as they ascend. All are coarsely toothed and hairy. Flowers in a leafy terminal panicle, bluish-purple. Of thickets and hedgerows, most frequent in the S. (Text Fig. 258). The giant campanula (*C. latifólia, broad-leaved*), rather similar with long and narrower leaves, has blue or white flowers, solitary in the axils of upper leaves, and is found in thickets in Scotland and N. England.

259. HARE- or HAIR-BELL (BLUEBELL in Scotland), *Campánula rotundifólia, round-leaved.* Summer to autumn.

A perennial, with an intricate running rootstock, up to 1½ ft. high. The more or less heart-shaped basal leaves which give the plant its name often die by the time that the blue or white flowers open. Of hill pastures, heaths, banks, and waysides. Widely distributed in Europe and W. Asia from the Mediterranean to the Arctic circle, and common in the N. of the U.S.A. and Canada (Text Fig. 259).

Many European and Asiatic, as well as some N. American, species are grown in gardens—particularly dwarf and mountain kinds in rock-gardens. The Canterbury bell (*C. médium, intermediate,* and its varieties) was brought from S. Europe in the sixteenth century. *Campánula* is from the Latin *campana,* a bell, from the shape of the flower. They are often called bell-flowers.

260. IVY-LEAVED BELLFLOWER, *Wahlenbérgia hederácea, ivy-like.* Summer to autumn.

A small, delicate, spreading perennial, with thread-like branches and flower-stems about 4 in. high. Of moist shady places, often along stream-sides, in fields and woods. Named after the German botanist G. Wahlenberg (1784–1814).

261. VENUS'S LOOKING-GLASS, *Speculária hýbrida, hybrid.* Late summer.

A branching annual, about 9 in. high. The sepals are longer than the petals. Of dry arable land, particularly in the E. counties.

H

The Venus's looking-glass of gardens is the continental *S. Spéculum* and its forms. *Speculária* is derived from the Latin *speculum*, a mirror, from the likeness of the flower to a looking-glass.

HEATH FAMILY: *Ericáceae*

A large family found in every continent except Australia, but particularly on moors, in swamps, and peaty districts in temperate and cool regions, with about 1,350 species.

It consists principally of shrubs with evergreen, leathery leaves, sometimes very small and creeping, at others tall and tree-like. The flowers

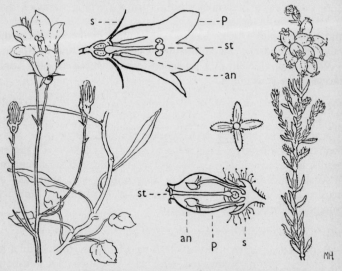

259. HARE-BELL   267. CROSS-LEAVED HEATH

have a corolla which is urn- or bell-shaped, dividing into four or five lobes, or in some cases consist of four or five almost distinct petals. The stamens are from eight to ten, and are connected to the sides of the corolla. Fruit a capsule or berry.

As a rule, the family is lime-hating; many kinds refuse to grow when even a trace of lime is present, probably because they need the presence of a fungus which only thrives in acid soils where there is decaying organic matter, such as peat or leaf-mould.

The strawberry-tree (*Árbutus Unédo*) is a shrub or tree from S. Europe and also native of S. Ireland; the sweet pepper (*Cléthra alnifólia, alder-leaved*) and mountain laurels (species of *Kálmia*) from N. America; *Pernéttya* from around the Straits of Magellan; and *Enkiánthus* from Japan, are some of the *Ericáceae* found in gardens. The family is of little economic importance.

Nos. 262 to 264 are often placed in a separate family, the *Vacciniáceae*; they are distinguished from the others by the relative position of the ovary.

262. BILBERRY, BLAEBERRY, WHORTLEBERRY, *Vaccínium Myrtíllus*. Spring.

A small, erect, deciduous shrub, with a creeping rootstock and angular, green branches about 1 ft. high. Berry round, almost black and covered with a light 'bloom,' surmounted by the remains of the calyx tube. Edible, 'one of the most valuable wild fruits in Britain.' —W. J. Bean. Abundant on moors and in woods on high land, except in the E. counties.

263. COWBERRY, RED WHORTLEBERRY, *Vaccínium Vítis-idaéa*. Early summer.

An evergreen creeping shrub, rather prostrate, about 9 in. high. Stems round and wiry. Fruit red, acid, but eaten cooked. Of moors, heaths, and open woods, most frequent in Scotland, and the mountains of Wales and N. England. The bog bilberry (*V. uliginósum,* of marshes), of heaths and bogs in the N., is differentiated from the common bilberry by its round stems.

264. CRANBERRY, *Oxycóccus palústris, of marshes*. Summer.

A prostrate, evergreen shrub with long wiry stems, thinner than in the previous plant. Berries red, pleasantly flavoured. Of peat-bogs in Scotland and the N. Drainage has reduced the area in which this plant grows. The 'cranberry' of shops often includes the fruit of other, often continental, species. The bearberry (*Arctostáphylós Úva-úrsi*), of dry heaths and hills in the N. and Ireland, is a procumbent evergreen shrub with red berries which have the remains of the calyx at the base instead of at the tip (as is the case with all the previously mentioned species) of the berry.

265. BOG ROSEMARY, *Andrómeda polifólia, with polished leaves*. Summer.

A low branching evergreen shrub, about 1 ft. high or less, the stem woody, creeping, and rooting. Of peat-bogs in C. and S. Scotland, and N. and C. England. Several close relatives are grown in gardens, particularly kinds of *Pieris*.

266. BELL, GREY, or SCOTCH HEATH, *Erica cinérea, grey*. Summer to autumn.

A low evergreen shrub, sometimes as much as $1\frac{1}{2}$ ft. high. Leaves three or four in a whorl. Has produced a number of different coloured varieties, including white, which are often grown in gardens. Of moors, often covering wide tracts.

267. CROSS-LEAVED HEATH, *Erica Tétralix*. Summer to early autumn.

A low evergreen shrub, from 6 in. to $1\frac{1}{2}$ ft. high, with leaves arranged in cross-shaped whorls of four. Flowers rose-coloured. Of moors and heaths, being the commonest *Erica* or true heath. It has produced several varieties, including a white-flowered form (Text Fig. 267). The wood of the large S. European tree heath (*E. arbórea, tree-like*) was once used for turning, particularly into 'briar' pipes—briar being a corruption of the French name *bruyère*.

268. LING, HEATHER, *Callúna vulgáris, common*. Summer.

An evergreen shrub usually between 1 ft. and 3 ft. high. Flowers pale pink, the calyx the same colour and giving the appearance of a double row of petals. At the base of the calyx are four small bracts. Very widely spread over the world, and covering extensive tracts of heath, moor, and mountain in Britain. It is variable in colour, and several selected forms are cultivated. From it, bees produce a distinctive honey, which does not crystallize as does other honey. The name is from the Greek *calluno*, to sweep, the twigs being used in besoms (Text Fig. 268).

269. WINTERGREEN, *Pýrola mínor, smaller*. Summer.

A partially evergreen perennial herb, with creeping rootstock. The leaves are leathery, forming a rosette, from which rises the flower-stem, about 9 in. high. Of moist woods and shady places in Scotland and N. England, local in the S. and rare in Ireland. *Pyrola* is derived from the Latin *pirus*, a pear, and alludes to a certain similarity in their leaves. The vegetable oil of wintergreen used for rheumatic complaints is obtained from an American plant, creeping wintergreen

264. CRANBERRY.   265. BOG ROSEMARY.   266. BELL HEATH.
269. WINTERGREEN.   271. PRIMROSE.   272. COWSLIP.
273. OXLIP.   274. BIRD'S-EYE   275. YELLOW LOOSE-
276. MONEYWORT.   PRIMROSE.   STRIFE.
                         278. SEA MILKWORT.   279. SCARLET PIMPERNEL.

(*Gaulthéria procúmbens, trailing*), of the same family, and also from an American birch.

270. COMMON RHODODENDRON, *Rhododéndron pónticum, of the coasts of the Black Sea.* Early summer.

A large evergreen shrub, with a spreading habit. Flowers purplish-pink. Leaves dark glossy-green above, much paler below. Introduced in 1763, native of Asia Minor, it is now one of our commonest

268. LING   270. COMMON RHODODENDRON

evergreens where lime is not present in the soil. It has been, in fact, rather too extensively and inappropriately planted.

Almost innumerable garden hybrids and species of rhododendron are cultivated; at Kew some four hundred species alone are grown out of doors. They come from Europe, Asia Minor, N. America, and particularly the Chino-Thibetan-Himalayan region, where a multitude of new kinds has been discovered during this century. They vary from small plants growing in exposed places in a manner similar to our own heaths to large trees found in sheltered forests. There are also tropical species. In these rhododendron districts, honey made from the flowers may be poisonous. The azaleas are, botanically speaking, deciduous species of rhododendron. The popular *Azálea móllis, soft,* hybrids are derived from *R. mólle*, native of China. They were introduced in 1823.

PRIMROSE FAMILY: *Primuláceae*

A family of perennial (some annual) herbs found chiefly in the N. hemisphere.

Leaves alternate or opposite, without stipules, and generally un-divided. Flower with five petals united at their base into a short tube, surrounded by five united sepals. The five stamens are each opposite a petal. A single slender style ends in a knob-like stigma. Fruit a capsule.

Several species of *Cýclamen*, both hardy and greenhouse, coming from S. Europe, Asia Minor, and N. Africa, are cultivated.

271. PRIMROSE, *Prímula vulgáris, common.* Spring.

Perennial about 6 in. high. The flowers are of two kinds, on separate plants, (i) *pin-eyed*, style long, the stigma held above the stamens which are deep in the throat of the flower, (ii) *thrum-eyed*, the style short, the stigma below the stamens, which are at the top of the throat. The inflorescence is a short-stalked umbel. Of hedgebanks and woods.

272. COWSLIP, PAIGLE, *Prímula véris, of spring.* Spring.

Perennial, flower-stem about 9 in. high, bearing flowers in an umbel. Of meadows, most frequent in England.

273. OXLIP, *Prímula elátior, taller.* Spring.

Perennial with stems up to 1 ft. high. The flowers have not the folding and thickening of the corolla present in the above two; this helps to distinguish it from hybrids between the primrose and cowslip, which are commonly known as false oxlips. The true oxlip is found in woods on limy soils in the S.-E. counties of England. The polyanthus is a cultivated form evolved from the foregoing primroses; several other varieties have long been grown in gardens.

274. BIRD'S-EYE PRIMROSE, *Prímula farinósa, mealy.* Summer.

A perennial about 6 in. high, with the underside of the leaves coated with a white mealy down. The whole plant has a more delicate appearance than any of the other primroses. Common locally in damp meadows in N. England.

Of recent years, many primulas have been introduced, particularly from China and Japan, and are often grown in gardens. The auricula (*P. Aurícula*), from the European alps, has been long cultivated in many forms. *Prímula* is from the Latin *primus*, first, alluding to its early flowering.

275. YELLOW LOOSESTRIFE, *Lysimáchia vulgáris, common*. Summer.

A perennial with a running rootstock which sends up flower-stems from 2 ft. to 4 ft. high. These bear numerous showy flowers in the axils of the upper leaves. Of river- and stream-sides and damp places, more particularly in England. No relative of the purple loosestrife (No. 144).

276. MONEYWORT, CREEPING JENNY, *Lysimáchia Nummulária*. Summer to autumn.

A trailing perennial, with stems up to 3 ft. long, rooting at the joints. Flowers showy. Of banks and moist, shady places; cultivated (particularly a golden-leaved form) in cottage gardens.

277. WOOD PIMPERNEL, *Lysimáchia némorum, of woods*. Summer.

A creeping plant, with slender rooting stems a few inches to 1 ft. long. Flowers yellow, small. The flower-stems curl round as the fruit ripens (Text Fig. 277).

278. SEA MILKWORT, BLACK SALTWORT, *Glaux marítima, of the sea*. Late spring to summer.

A low branching perennial with a creeping rootstock, the stems from 3 in. to 6 in. or so high. Leaves small and fleshy; the upper surface a dark, the lower surface a pale, blue-green. The flower has a coloured calyx, but no petals. Of sea-shores, salt marshes, and of inland salt areas in the midlands. Name from Greek *glaukos*, sea-green.

279. SCARLET PIMPERNEL, POOR MAN'S WEATHER-GLASS, *Anagállis arvénsis, of cultivated fields*. Spring to autumn.

A branched, spreading annual, with erect branches sometimes 1 ft. high. Flowers small, and closing in the afternoon and in bad weather. The flower-stalk rolls back when the seeds ripen. A weed of cultivation spread by man to many parts of the world. There are less common pink, white, and blue forms.

280. Bog Pimpernel, *Anagállis tenélla, delicate.* Summer.

A small, slender, creeping perennial, with stems a few inches long, rooting as they go. Flowers rose-coloured on delicate stems, and much larger than on the scarlet pimpernel. Of moist banks, damp heaths, and bogs (Text Fig. 280).

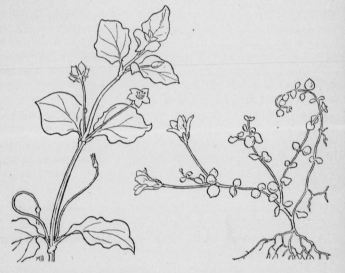

277. WOOD PIMPERNEL   280. BOG PIMPERNEL

281. Brookweed, *Sámolus Valerándi.* Summer to autumn.

Perennial, with a tuft of radical leaves from which rise the flower-stems 3 in. to 1 ft. high. Of damp places, usually near the sea and along the west coast.

BUTTERWORT FAMILY: *Lentibulariáceae*

A small family of marsh or aquatic plants spread over the world, usually insectivorous.

Leaves in a rosette and entire, or when submerged, finely divided. Flowers on a leafless stalk. The corolla has five petals united at the base, with two lips and a spur. Stamens, two. Fruit a one-celled capsule.

282. BUTTERWORT, *Pinguícula vulgáris, common.* Early summer.

Perennial with a rosette of rather succulent leaves which are covered with glands which exude a sticky fluid. Small insects caught on this set up an irritation which causes the leaf to roll up; an acid fluid is then produced which dissolves the insect, the plant absorbing the juices. The flower⁄stems are in a cluster, up to 6 in. high. Replaced in the S.⁄W. by *P. lusitanica, Portuguese,* smaller and paler. Name from Latin *pinguis,* fat, from the greasy leaves.

283. SMALL BLADDERWORT, *Utriculária mínor, smaller.* Summer.

Perennial, floating on water. The stems are root⁄like, often intri⁄ cately branched, and bear finely divided submerged leaves. In the leaf axils are borne small 'bladders,' about one⁄twelfth of an inch long. These trap minute water insects, on which, as they decay, the plant feeds. The flower⁄stems project about 3 in. out of the water. Of still pools and ditches, particularly on moorlands. The common bladder⁄ wort (*U. vulgáris, common*) is similar but larger, the flower⁄stems being up to 8 in. long, with fewer and larger yellow flowers. Name from Latin *utriculus,* bladder.

OLIVE FAMILY: *Oleáceae*

A family of woody plants found mostly in tropical and warm temperate climates.

In Britain, trees and shrubs with opposite leaves, either simple and entire, or pinnately compound, without stipules. Flowers with a four⁄ or five⁄lobed calyx and a tubular corolla, also divided into four or five lobes. The two stamens are always joined to the base of the corolla. Fruit a berry, capsule, or winged 'key.'

The olive itself, native of Asia Minor and Syria, can only be grown out of doors in the mildest parts of Britain, but hardy and popular members of the family include the lilacs, cultivated forms derived principally from *Syrínga vulgáris, common,* of S.⁄E. Europe, which has been grown in Britain for three centuries; the winter jessamine (*Jasmínum nudiflórum, flowering when leafless*), introduced from China a century ago; the climbing jessamine (*J. officinále, of use to man*), a native of Persia and N.⁄W. India, grown in Britain since the sixteenth century; and the more recently introduced *Forsythia* from China.

284. COMMON ASH, *Fráxinus excélsior, loftier.* Spring.

One of the largest native deciduous trees, sometimes reaching 140 ft.

It is graceful in form, with a pale bark fissured longitudinally. Young wood greenish-grey. Flowers, before the leaves open, are without calyx or corolla. Timber valuable, white, light, tough, and easily bent. Used particularly in frames for carriage-body building and aircraft, agricultural implements, and sports goods. It is usually the last native tree to open its leaves in spring. Several ornamental varieties such as the weeping and one-leaved (in which the terminal leaflet alone is usually developed) are planted.

285. COMMON PRIVET, *Ligústrum vulgáre, common.* Summer.

A more or less evergreen shrub, according to situation, reaching 10 ft. or so high. Flowers heavily scented, white. Fruit a small black berry. Truly wild in the S. on cliffs and chalk soils. The Japanese *L. ovalifólium, oval-leaved,* which is rather more evergreen, has practically replaced it in garden hedges. Name from Latin *ligo*, to tie, referring to the use of the supple twigs to tie up faggots.

PERIWINKLE FAMILY: *Apocynáceae*

A large family, for the most part tropical. Only represented in Britain by periwinkles, and some tender or greenhouse plants such as the rose-bay or oleander (*Nérium Oleánder*) from the Mediterranean region.

286. LESSER PERIWINKLE, *Vínca minor, smaller.* Spring to autumn.

An evergreen shrub with a creeping rootstock and long, trailing, pliable branches, which root at the joints. The flower-stems are erect, about 1 ft. high, bearing a single flower about 1 in. across, usually blue, though not infrequently white or pink. Fruit a capsule. Native of Europe, and perhaps an introduced plant in Britain, where it is found on shady banks, mostly near gardens. Several forms, such as the double, are cultivated. The greater periwinkle (*V. májor, greater*) is also a European plant often found around gardens. It has arching stems, larger leaves, and fewer flowers about 2 in. across. Name from Latin *vincire*, to bind, from the use of the stems.

GENTIAN FAMILY: *Gentianáceae*

A cosmopolitan family of herbs, but found chiefly in temperate climates and among mountains. Some of its members are found at the highest limits of vegetation.

The leaves are usually opposite and entire (except in *Menyánthes*), without stipules. The calyx divided usually into four or five, but sometimes eight to ten, segments. The corolla is tubular, parting into as many lobes as the calyx has divisions. Stamens between each divi-sion of the corolla. Fruit a capsule. The parts of the plants usually taste bitter.

287. COMMON CENTAURY, *Erythraéa Centaúrium*. Summer.

An erect annual with a square stem from a few inches to 1 ft. high. The lower leaves form a spreading tuft. Of dry fields and sandy places,

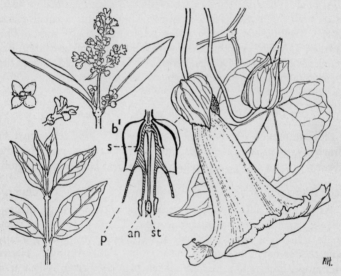

285. COMMON PRIVET   291. GREAT BINDWEED

particularly in the S. Several forms are usually differentiated into distinct species. Name from Greek *erutheros,* red, referring to the flower-colour. Not to be confused with *Centauréa* (Nos. 237–9).

288. FIELD GENTIAN, *Gentiána campéstris, of the plains*. Autumn.

An erect annual about 6 in. high. The parts of the flowers are in fours, and the fringe at the mouth of the corolla conspicuous. Two of the sepals are much larger than the others. Of pastures and commons, particularly in hilly ground on chalk soils. Felwort or autumn gentian

(*G. Amarélla*) is an annual similar in appearance to the last, but generally taller and with the parts of the flowers often in fives and nearly
equal sepals.   The garden gentianella is *G. acaúlis, stemless*, a very
variable species from C. Europe.   Many other alpine kinds from
Europe, China, and Thibet, are grown, particularly in rock-gardens.
Nearly all are distinguished by the brilliant blue of their flowers.
The gentians were long used in medicine.   The continental yellow-
flowered *G. lútea, yellow*, provides a simple bitter tonic.   Named after
Gentius, King of Illyria.

289. BUCKBEAN, MARSH TREFOIL, *Menyánthes trifoliáta, three-leaved*.
    Early summer.

Perennial, growing only in marshes and shallow water, the rootstock creeping in the mud.   Stems creeping or floating, up to 1 ft.
long.   Flowers, five-lobed and fringed inside, of two types on separate
plants, to ensure cross-fertilization, (i) styles long, stamens short;
(ii) styles short, stamens long.   The rootstock was once much used as
a bitter tonic.

BINDWEED FAMILY: *Convolvuláceae*

A family of herbs (many climbing), shrubs, and a few trees, spread
over the tropical and temperate regions of the world.   One genus is
parasitic.   Often containing latex.

In Britain twining or creeping herbs, either with alternate leaves, or,
when parasitic, without green leaves.   No stipules.   Sepals four or
five, separate.   Corolla bell- or urn-shaped with four or five lobes.
Stamens four or five, attached near the base of the corolla (Text Fig.
291, inset).   Fruit a capsule.

It includes greenhouse climbers such as *Ipómaea* from tropical
America, although *I. purpúrea, purple*, is a hardy annual, better known as
morning glory.   Otherwise the family recalls mostly troublesome weeds
and parasites.

290. SMALL BINDWEED, *Convólvulus arvénsis, of cultivated fields*.
    Summer to early autumn.

A perennial with a creeping rootstock which spreads rapidly underground, difficult to eradicate as small broken pieces will grow.   Stems
twining or trailing, not usually above 3 ft. long.   Flowers scented and
closing at night or in bad weather.   Of fields and banks, rare in
Scotland.

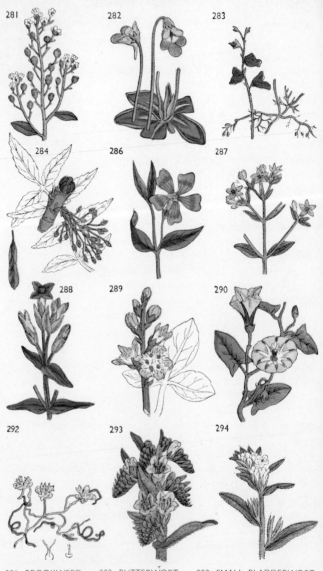

281. BROOKWEED.   282. BUTTERWORT.   283. SMALL BLADDERWORT.
284. COMMON ASH.   286. LESSER PERI-
                       WINKLE.   287. COMMON CENTAURY.
288. FIELD GENTIAN.   289. BUCKBEAN.   290. SMALL BINDWEED.
292. LESSER DODDER.   293. VIPER'S BUGLOSS. 294. CORN GROMWELL.

291. GREAT BINDWEED, *Convólvulus sépium, dark brown*. Summer.

Perennial, similar in growth to the last, but much stronger, the stems climbing to a height of several feet. The large flower is white or tinted with pink, and does not shut so readily. It is enclosed at the base by two large bracts (inset b^1). Of hedgerows and a weed of cultivated ground (Text Fig. 291). The sea-bindweed (*C. Soldan-élla*), a plant of sandy shores, has a creeping rootstock and two bracts at the base of the large pink flower, but has short, prostrate stems and rather fleshy leaves. In gardens 'convolvulus major' is really morning glory (see family, above). The dwarf bedding convolvulus, called 'convolvulus minor,' is *C. trícolor, three - coloured*, from S. - W. Europe, which has been long cultivated. Name from Latin *convolvere*, to entwine.

292. LESSER or HEATH DODDER, *Cúscuta Epithýmum*. Late summer.

A parasitic annual without green leaves, attaching itself to the stems of furze, heaths, and thyme by sucker-like roots. The crimson stems are thread-like, and the flowers, in small globular heads, are minute. One or two other species, similar in general appearance, are sometimes found.

BORAGE FAMILY: *Boragináceae*

A family consisting chiefly of herbs, distributed in tropical and temperate regions, particularly the N. hemisphere and especially around the Mediterranean.

In Britain, herbs, usually roughly hairy. Leaves alternate, simple, and generally entire, without stipules. The flowers, in cymes, have five sepals joined at the base. The corolla is more or less bell-shaped; tubular at the base, dividing into five petals. The throat is frequently thickened into scales, or hairy. The colour is often blue or bluish-pink. Five stamens attached to the corolla tube alternate with the petals. The fruit consists of four separate nutlets.

European species of lungwort (*Pulmonária*) have long been cultivated in gardens and are sometimes found apparently wild. They are per-ennials with rather rough, deep-green leaves blotched with white. The flowers vary from blue to pink. Once a valued chest medicine.

293. VIPER'S BUGLOSS, *Échium vulgáre, common*. Summer.

A biennial, bristly in all its parts, with an erect stem about 2 ft. high. Radical leaves long and stalked. Flowers pink at first, becoming blue.

A handsome plant, not to be confused with the rather undistinguished common bugloss (No. 299).

294. CORN GROMWELL, BASTARD ALKANET, *Lithospérmum arvénse, of cultivated fields.* Spring to summer.

An erect, hairy, branching annual about 1 ft. high. A weed of cultivation and waste places. Nutlets very hard and wrinkled.

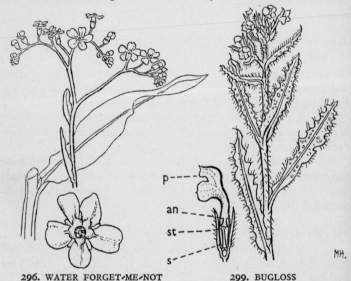

p
an
st
s

296. WATER FORGET-ME-NOT   299. BUGLOSS

MH.

295. GROMWELL, *Lithospérmum officinále, of use to man.* Spring to summer.

Perennial, resembling the last but stronger and taller, with smaller flowers and leaves with prominent veins. Nutlets are hard and white, and, when fresh, without wrinkles. Waste places and way-sides, not common in Scotland. Name, from the Greek *lithos,* stone, and *sperma,* seed, refers to the hard fruit.

296. WATER FORGET-ME-NOT, *Myosótis scorpioídes, the inflorescence curled like a scorpion's tail.* Summer.

Perennial with a somewhat creeping rootstock and rather weak stems up to 2 ft. high. Flowers bright blue with a yellow eye. Calyx with adpressed hairs, never deeply divided as it is in the other species. Of stream-sides and moist places (Text Fig. 296).

297. FIELD FORGET-ME-NOT, *Myosótis arvénsis, of cultivated fields.* Summer to autumn.

A branching hairy annual, between 6 in. and 1½ ft. high. Lower leaves oblong, narrowing to stalks. Calyx with spreading hairs, divided to half its length. Of fields, waste places, banks, etc. The commonest species.

298. YELLOW-AND-BLUE SCORPION-GRASS, *Myosótis versícolor, of changing colour.* Spring.

A small annual with a simple erect hairy stem rising up to about 1 ft. high from a tuft of leaves. Flowers small, pale yellow on opening, becoming blue. On banks and waste land. Early scorpion-grass (*M. collína, of low hills*) is a small annual a few inches high with bright blue flowers in spring, found on dry banks, sand dunes, and other open places.

All myosotis were known as scorpion-grass formerly, but the name forget-me-not has now become popular—it once belonged to the speed-well. Name from Greek *mus*, mouse, and *ous*, ear, from the form or texture of the leaves.

299. BUGLOSS, *Lycópsis arvénsis, of cultivated fields.* Summer.

A spreading annual up to 1½ ft. high, thickly covered with stiff hairs. Flower small, blue, with a white eye. A field weed (Text Fig. 299).

300. COMFREY, *Sýmphytum officinále, of use to man.* Summer.

A perennial with a spreading tough rootstock (difficult to eradicate) sending up rough stems from 2 ft. to 3 ft. high. Lower leaves stalked, upper running down the stem as wings. Flower varies from dull white or yellow to dull pink or purple. Of damp shady places and moist meadows. Once famous for healing wounds (name from Greek *sumphuo*, to make grow together) and as a chest medicine (Text Fig.300).

301. BORAGE, *Borágo officinális, of use to man.* Summer to early autumn.

An annual or biennial with spreading growth, about 1 ft. high. Flowers a brilliant blue or sometimes white, with dark purple anthers, and attractive to bees. Once used as a medicine for melancholy, and

more recently in salads or drinks. It smells rather of cucumber. Not
a native, but often found around gardens. It was introduced long ago
from the E. Mediterranean (Text Fig. 301).

302. HOUND'S-TONGUE, *Cynoglóssum officinále, of use to man.* Summer.

A biennial with a branching hairy stem about 2 ft. high thrown up
from a tuft of oval leaves the second year. Fruit hooked and spread by

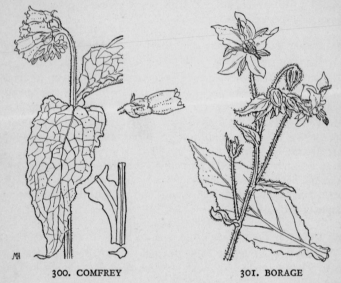

300. COMFREY   301. BORAGE

animals. The plant has an unpleasant smell. Of waste places and
roadsides from mid-Scotland southwards. Name from Greek *kion*,
dog, and *glossa*, tongue, from the texture of the leaves.

NIGHTSHADE FAMILY: *Solanáceae*

A family of herbs, shrubs, and small trees associated particularly with
the tropical and temperate parts of C. and S. America. Several of its
members are of great economic importance, providing foodstuffs and
valuable drugs.

Leaves alternate without stipules. The flower, carried singly or in
forked cymes, have usually a five-lobed calyx and a corolla in one piece
dividing into five lobes. The fruit is a berry or capsule.

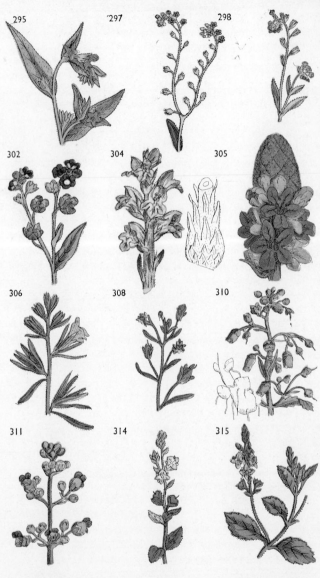

295. GROMWELL.
302. HOUND'S-
     TONGUE.
306. LESSER SNAP-
     DRAGON.
311. WATER FIG-
     WORT.

297. FIELD FORGET-
     ME-NOT.
304. GREAT BROOM-
     RAPE
308. SMALL TOAD-FLAX.
314. THYME-LEAVED
     SPEEDWELL.

298. YELLOW-AND-
     BLUE SCORPION-
     GRASS.
305. GREAT MULLEIN.
310. FIGWORT.
315. COMMON SPEED-
     WELL.

It includes two plants, both quite uncommon, which are among the most poisonous in Britain. Deadly nightshade or dwale (*Átropa Belladónna*) is occasionally found in waste places near old dwellings or ruins, particularly in chalky soils. The whole plant has an un-pleasant smell. It is a bushy herbaceous perennial about 3 ft. high, with dark-green leaves, egg-shaped and broadly pointed, having entire edges. Flowers, in late summer, single on a drooping stalk, dull purple. Berries black and shining, the size of a cherry. The whole plant is poisonous whether fresh, dried, or boiled. The fleshy rootstock yields the alkaloid drug atropine, which paralyses the nerve-ends. Its power of dilating the pupil of the eye is well known, and is the origin of the name *Belladónna* (beautiful woman), having been used as a beauty preparation. Henbane (*Hyoscýamus níger, black*) is an occasional plant of waste land near buildings. It is a hairy and sticky annual or biennial, about 2 ft. high, with egg-shaped notched leaves. The flowers, in summer, in a double row, are yellow with purplish veins. It has a bad smell, and poisonous qualities similar to nightshade. It yields the alkaloid hyoscyamine, a strong narcotic.

303. BITTERSWEET, WOODY NIGHTSHADE, *Solánum Dulcamára*. Summer to early autumn.

A perennial with creeping rootstock sending up semi-woody, trailing stems, which to some extent die back in winter. The flowers are very similar to the potato, purple with noticeable yellow anthers, in loose cymes. The bright-red berries are showy. Of hedgerows and among bushes. The stem if chewed tastes first bitter and then sweet. But the whole plant is best considered poisonous, the berries, attractive to children, particularly so (Text Fig. 303, inset flower to same scale). Black nightshade (*S. nígrum, black*) is a common weed of cultivated land, though less common in the N. It is biennial or annual, with spreading branches a foot or two high, with egg-shaped leaves having coarse angular teeth. Flowers, in summer and autumn, white, small, in small contracted cymes. The rounded berries are usually black. This plant and its berries, too, should be considered poisonous; the strong smell may be a warning. Both the above are often confused with the true nightshade already mentioned, but as long as all are re-garded as highly poisonous, no harm will be done.

The potato is the most important member of this genus. It is derived from *S. tuberósum, tuberous,* and probably other species native of the temperate parts of the Andes. The same poison (the alkaloid *solanine*) found in all the above is present in its berries and in the green, unripened tubers. It was introduced into England during the six-teenth century (untraditionally, not by Raleigh).

The tomato or love-apple (*S. Lycopérsicum*) was introduced from S. America as a decorative plant in the sixteenth century, but the fruit was not generally eaten until the nineteenth.

BROOMRAPE FAMILY: *Orobanchάceae*

A small family of parasitic herbs distributed chiefly in temperate climates.

The plants are brown, yellow, purplish or blue, but never green, and have scales instead of leaves. They grow on the roots of their host, and send up simple flowering spikes alone.

Toothwort (*Lathraéa squamária, scaly*), rather similar to orabanche below, with flesh- or lilac-coloured flowers and a rootstock covered with fleshy scales, is sometimes found growing from the roots of trees.

304. GREAT BROOMRAPE, *Orobánche májor, greater*. Early summer.

Stem from 1 ft. to 2 ft. high, at first yellow, becoming a dull purple. Parasitic on leguminous plants, particularly broom. Several other species, all bearing a family likeness, but mostly smaller than the last, are occasionally found parasitic on a variety of plants. *Orobánche* is from the Greek *orobus*, vetch, and *anchein*, choke, alluding to the hosts of certain species.

FIGWORT FAMILY: *Scrophulariáceae*

A large family, mostly herbs and under-shrubs, distributed from the Arctic to the tropics. Nearly all are poisonous.

In Britain, herbs with alternate or opposite leaves without stipule. The typical flower is described on page 10 and Plate III. Fruit a capsule.

The family is of little economic value, but a number of its exotic members are cultivated for their flowers, including species and varieties of *Calceolária* and *Péntstemon*, both from S. America. The rock-garden *Erínus alpínus, of high mountains*, from S.-W. Europe, is found on the Roman Wall, and is traditionally said to have been introduced by the Romans.

305. GREAT MULLEIN, AARON'S ROD, *Verbáscum Thápsus.* Summer.

An erect biennial up to 4 ft. high, covered with woolly hairs. The basal leaves are large and broadly lance-shaped, with stalks, the stem leaves run down the stem as wings. Flowers in a spike as much as a foot long. Of waysides and waste places. European and Asiatic kinds, similar in general character but varying in height and colour of flower, are grown in gardens.

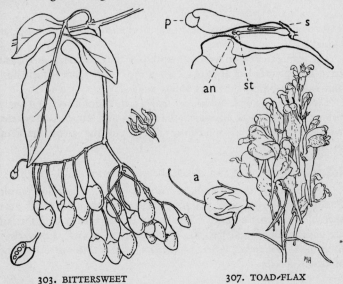

303. BITTERSWEET   307. TOAD-FLAX

306. LESSER SNAPDRAGON, WEASEL'S SNOUT, *Antirrhínum Orón-tium.* Summer to autumn.

A slender erect annual about 1 ft. high. A weed of cultivation, of gravelly or sandy soils, most usual in the S. The garden snapdragon has been evolved from *A. május, great,* a plant of stony places and walls in the Mediterranean regions. In some places in Britain it has become naturalized in similar situations.

307. TOAD-FLAX, BUTTER-AND-EGGS, *Linária vulgáris, common.* Summer to autumn.

Perennial with a creeping rootstock, with erect stems from 1 ft. to 3 ft. high. Flowers yellow. Of hedgerows and field-sides (Text Fig. 307, inset *a,* fruit).

308. SMALL TOADFLAX, *Linária mínor, smaller.* Spring to autumn.

A branched erect annual, a few inches up to 1 ft. high. A weed of cultivation in gardens and fields on sandy or chalk soils and railway tracks in England, less common in Scotland.

309. IVY-LEAVED TOADFLAX, *Linária Cymbálaria.* Summer to autumn.

A trailing perennial, a few inches high. Flowers lilac, the lip yellow. Not native, but widely established in and around gardens,

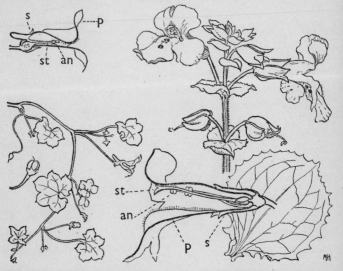

309. IVY-LEAVED TOADFLAX   312. YELLOW MIMULUS

on walls, and stony places (Text Fig. 309). *Linária* is from Latin *linum,* flax, which the leaves of some kinds resemble.

310. FIGWORT, KNOTTED FIGWORT, *Scrophulária nodósa, with swollen joints.* Summer to autumn.

A perennial with a knotted tuberous rootstock which sends up an erect, branching, four-angled stem up to 3 ft. high. Leaves large, heart-shaped, pointed and doubly toothed. The plant has an unpleasant smell which is, however, attractive to wasps—it is one of the few flowers they fertilize. Of moist, shady waste and cultivated ground. Once used as a remedy for scrofula.

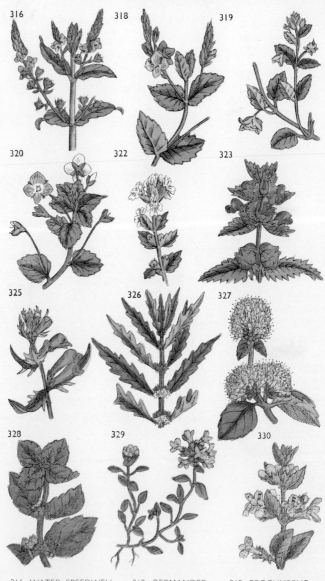

316. WATER SPEEDWELL.
320. BUXBAUM'S
    SPEEDWELL.
325. COMMON COW-
    WHEAT.
328. CORN MINT.

318. GERMANDER
    SPEEDWELL.
322. EYEBRIGHT.
326. GIPSY-WORT.
329. WILD THYME.

319. PROCUMBENT
    SPEEDWELL.
323. YELLOW-RATTLE.
327. WATER MINT.
330. COMMON CALA-
    MINT.

311. WATER FIGWORT, WATER BETONY, *Scrophulária aquática, of water*. Summer.

Very similar to the above, but usually much taller. The stem is winged, there are no tubers at its base, and the leaves are narrower. Of stream-sides and wet places. The name is derived from the use of No. 310.

312. YELLOW MIMULUS, MONKEY-FLOWER, *Mimulus guttátus, spotted*. Summer to autumn.

A perennial with a creeping rootstock and stems about 1 ft. high. Flowers yellow, usually spotted with red. Of stream-sides and shady wet places. A native of N.-W. America, but long cultivated and extensively naturalized (Text Fig. 312). The musk mimulus (*M. moschátus, musky*) was also brought from N.-W. America; it was famous for its scent, which has now unaccountably disappeared. Other kinds also are cultivated. Name from Greek *mimo*, an ape, alluding to the shape of the flower.

313. FOXGLOVE, *Digitális purpúrea, purple*. Spring to summer.

A biennial, though sometimes flowering a second or third time, with a rosette of stalked, downy leaves. Flowering stems from 2 ft. to 4 ft. or sometimes more. The flowers are purple, occasionally white. The plant is poisonous in all its parts, fresh or dried. The leaves yield the valuable drug known as digitalis, used particularly to stimulate the heart muscles and promote the circulation. (Text Fig. 313). The yellow foxglove (*D. ambígua, doubtful*), grown in gardens, comes from C. Europe. Name from Latin *digitus*, a finger, from the shape of the flowers.

314. THYME-LEAVED SPEEDWELL, *Verónica serpyllifólia, thyme-leaved*. Spring to summer.

A creeping perennial, forming a densely leaved, much-branched, flat tuft a few inches high, the stems rooting as they run and turning up at the tips. Leaves three-nerved. Of open woods, pastures, and waysides.

315. COMMON SPEEDWELL, *Verónica officinális, of use to man*. Summer.

Perennial, with hairy creeping and rooting stems a few inches to 1 ft. long. Of open woods and dry pastures. Once used to make a 'tea.'

316. WATER SPEEDWELL, *Verónica Anagállis*. Summer.

A perennial with a creeping rootstock. Stems stout, hollow, and fleshy about 2 ft. high. Leaves without stalks. In streams, ditches, and along water-sides.

317. BROOKLIME, *Verónica Beccabúnga*. Summer.

Perennial, the stems running or floating and rooting at their base, the flowering branches erect and fleshy. Flowers bright blue or some-

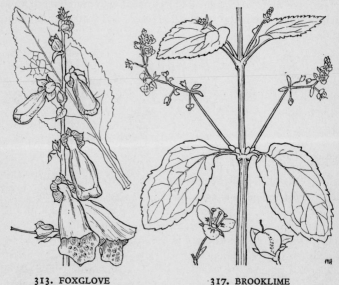

313. FOXGLOVE   317. BROOKLIME

times pink. Leaves with short stalks. Of streams, ditches, and along water-sides (Text Fig. 317).

318. GERMANDER SPEEDWELL, *Verónica Chamaédrys*. Spring to summer.

Perennial, the stems first creeping and rooting, then ascending to about 1 ft. The branches have two lines of hairs. Of open woods, pastures, and waysides.

319. PROCUMBENT or LESSER FIELD SPEEDWELL, *Verónica agréstis*, of the field. Spring to autumn.

A hairy, branching, and more or less prostrate annual, with small leaves and flowers. One of the commonest weeds of cultivated and waste places.

320. Buxbaum's or Greater Field Speedwell, *Verónica pérsica,*
 Persian. Spring to autumn.

Very similar to the above but larger, the flowers especially so and
of a brighter blue. Also a weed of cultivation and waste land, but
perhaps introduced from S. Europe or Asia. Wall speedwell (*V.
arvénsis, of cultivated fields*), a small hairy annual with heart-shaped leaves
having rounded teeth and small pale-blue flowers with a white centre,

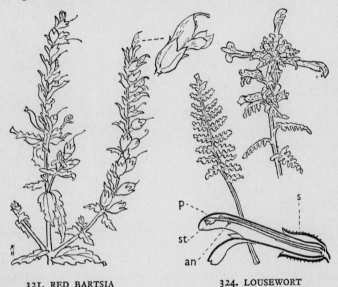

321. RED BARTSIA   324. LOUSEWORT

is found in walls, on banks, and dry waste or cultivated land. Mountain speedwell (*V. montána, of mountains*) is a perennial similar in appearance to germander speedwell, but with stalked leaves and stems hairy all
round. Of moist and shady places. Ivy-leaved speedwell (*V. hederae-
folia, ivy-leaved*) is a small annual weed with stalked, lobed (not serrated)
leaves, the axils of which bear single stalked pale-blue flowers.

321. Red Bartsia, Red Eyebright, *Bártsia Odontítes.* Summer.

An erect, branching annual about 9 in. high, with a wiry four-
angled stem. Flower dull red. Partially parasitic on the roots of
other plants. Of fields and waste places (Text Fig. 321). Varying

forms are sometimes differentiated as distinct species. Named after an early eighteenth-century German botanist, John Bartsch.

322. EYEBRIGHT, *Euphrásia officinális, of use to man.* Summer to autumn.

A small annual, partially parasitic on the roots of grasses, and vary-ing remarkably in size and form according to its situations, from 2 in. to 8 in. high. The flowers are sometimes almost completely yellow. Of grassland. Once used to make an eye lotion; the name from the Greek *euphraino*, I gladden, refers to its beneficial qualities.

323. YELLOW-RATTLE, *Rhinánthus Crísta-gálli.* Summer to autumn.

An annual, erect, from an inch or two to 1 ft. high. Parasitic on the roots of grasses. Corolla sometimes has a purple spot on the lips. Like the last, a variable plant according to situation. Found in association with grass, and, where common, damaging to it. Name from Greek *rhinos*, nose, and *anthos*, flower, from the shape of the flower.

324. LOUSEWORT, *Pediculáris sylvática, of woods.* Spring to summer.

A small perennial, about 6 in. or less high, easily recognized by its fern-like foliage. Flower pinkish-red or rarely white. Of damp heaths and open woods, where it is partially parasitic on roots (Text Fig. 324). Name from Latin *pediculus*, louse, an extract from the plant having been used against vermin.

325. COMMON or YELLOW COW-WHEAT, *Melampýrum praténse, of meadows.* Summer to autumn.

An annual with an erect branching stem from 6 in. to 1 ft. high. Leaves very narrow, in pairs. Of dry heaths and open woods. Partly parasitic on the roots of other plants. Name from Greek *melas*, black, and *puros*, wheat, from the appearance of the seeds.

MINT OR LABIATE FAMILY: *Labiátae*

A large family with about 3,000 species distributed over the world, but particularly in the Mediterranean regions. They are mostly herbs, a number being marsh plants, though some are shrubs.

The stems are square. Leaves opposite, usually undivided, without stipules. The flower is described on page 10 and Plate III. The inflorescence in the axils of the upper leaves has the appearance of being whorled, but actually each whorl consists of a pair of opposite cymes. Fruit a nutlet.

Most labiates have a strong scent, often aromatic but sometimes objectionable. The volatile oils of some are valuable in medicine and perfumery, while several are used as seasonings and condiments. Mediterranean species grown in herb gardens include sweet marjoram (*Oríganum Marjorána*, pot marjoram, *O. vulgáre, common*, is a British native), sage (*Sálvia officinális, of use to man*), and lavender (*Lavandúla véra, true*). Among numerous other cultivated species are the greenhouse *Cóleus*, with its brilliantly coloured foliage, from the E. Indies, etc.; rosemary (*Rosmarínus officinális, of use to man*) from S. Europe and Asia Minor, one of our oldest introduced plants; several other ornamental sages (*Sálvia*) from America and elsewhere; and the fragrant bergamot or Oswego tea (*Monárda didýma, in pairs*) from N. America.

326. GIPSY-WORT, *Lýcopus europaéus, European*. Summer.

A perennial with a creeping rootstock and tall, branching stems about 3 ft. high. Flowers very numerous but insignificant. Of ditches and watersides.

327. WATER MINT, *Méntha aquática, of water*. Late summer to autumn.

Perennial with a creeping rootstock sending out many runners. Stems numerous from 2 ft. to 3 ft. high. Aromatic. Marshes and wet places.

328. CORN MINT, *Méntha arvénsis, of cultivated fields*. Autumn.

Perennial with suckering rootstock and many spreading branches, from 6 in. to 1 ft. or more high. Of arable fields. Aromatic.

Mints are rather variable plants, and besides the above a few other species are found in Britain, which hybridize freely with one another. The spearmint from which sauce is made is *M. víridis, green*, while peppermint is *M. piperíta, pepper-like*. Both are cultivated and sometimes found wild. All mints are to varying extents aromatic, and usually found in moist places. Called after the nymph Minthe.

329. WILD THYME, *Thýmus Serpýllum*. Summer.

A perennial, densely branched, a few inches high, almost woody at the base, forming tufts or mats sometimes over a foot in diameter. Of banks, dry heaths, and stony places. The thyme cultivated in gardens as a herb is *T. vulgáris, common*, and its varieties, from S. Europe.

330. COMMON CALAMINT, *Calamíntha officinális, of use to man.* Summer.

A perennial with creeping rootstock, stems hairy, with long branches up to 3 ft. high. Of woods, hedgerows, and waysides. Name from Greek *kalos*, beautiful, and *minthe*, mint.

331. GROUND-IVY, *Népeta hederácea, ivy-like.* Early spring to early summer.

A perennial with creeping stems which root at the joints. From

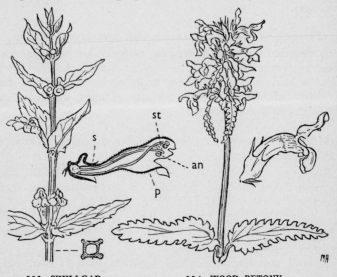

333. SKULLCAP   **334. WOOD BETONY**

6 in. to 1 ft. high. Of shady places. It was once used in brewing. The catmint of gardens is *N. Mussínii*, from the Caucasus.

332. SELF-HEAL, *Prunélla vulgáris, common.* Summer to autumn.

A perennial with creeping and rooting stems. Flower-stems ascending and usually a few inches high, but in mown grass only an inch. In grassy places, particularly if moist. Once much used as a medicine, internally and externally, for wounds.

333. SKULLCAP, *Scutellária galericuláta, with a hood.* Summer.

A perennial with a creeping rootstock and branched, erect stems from 8 in. to 1 ft. or more high. Flowers dull blue. Of watersides and moist shady places (Text Fig. 333). Lesser skullcap (*S. mínor, smaller*) is a miniature of the above. Stems 6 in. long, with pink flowers, found on wet heaths, flowering in late summer. Name from Latin *scutella*, a dish, from the shape of the calyx.

334. WOOD BETONY, *Stáchys officinális, of use to man*. Summer.

A hairy perennial up to 2 ft. high. Calyx teeth stiff and prickly. Flowers reddish-purple. Of woodsides, thickets, and pastures (Text Fig. 334).

335. HEDGE WOUNDWORT, *Stáchys sylvática, of woods*. Summer.

A perennial with a short creeping rootstock and a strong, erect, solid, branching stem up to 4 ft. high but usually less. The whole plant is hairy, and has a strong, unpleasant smell. Flowers dark reddish-purple, the lip marked in white. Ditches, woodsides, and shady places (Text Fig. 335).

336. MARSH WOUNDWORT, *Stáchys palústris, of marshes*. Summer to autumn.

Similar to above in growth, but less hairy, with a hollow stem, narrower leaves, and paler flowers. Of ditches and moist, shady places.

337. FIELD or CORN WOUNDWORT, *Stáchys arvénsis, of cultivated fields*. Spring to late autumn.

A small, spreading hairy annual, branching from the base, only a few inches high. Quite different in appearance to the above wound-worts. Of fields and waste places. Name from Greek *stachys*, a spike, alluding to the inflorescence.

338. RED HEMP-NETTLE, *Galeópsis Ládanum*. Summer to autumn.

An annual with spreading branches, softly downy, about 9 in. high. The stems are not swollen at the joints. Of cultivated fields and waste places, particularly in the S.

339. COMMON HEMP-NETTLE, *Galeópsis Tétrahit*. Summer to autumn.

An annual, usually much larger than the last, with hairy branches which are swollen below the joints. In cultivated fields and waste places. Name from Greek *galea*, weasel, and *opsis*, appearance, from a likeness of the flower to a weasel's head.

340. HENBIT DEAD-NETTLE, *Lámium amplexicaúle, with stem-clasping leaves.* Late spring to autumn.

A spreading, much-branched annual, a few inches high. The

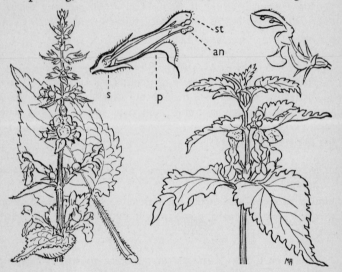

335. HEDGE WOUNDWORT   342. WHITE DEAD-NETTLE

lower leaves are rounded and on stalks. They are not so deeply cut as the upper. Of cultivated and waste land.

341. RED DEAD-NETTLE, *Lámium purpúreum, purple.* Early spring to autumn.

Similar in growth and lower leaves to the last, but the upper leaves are all shortly stalked and heart-shaped or almost triangular. In cultivated and waste land.

342. WHITE DEAD-NETTLE, *Lámium álbum, white.* Early spring to autumn.

A spreading perennial with a slightly creeping rootstock. Stems hairy, about 1 ft. high. Flowers white and downy on the hood.

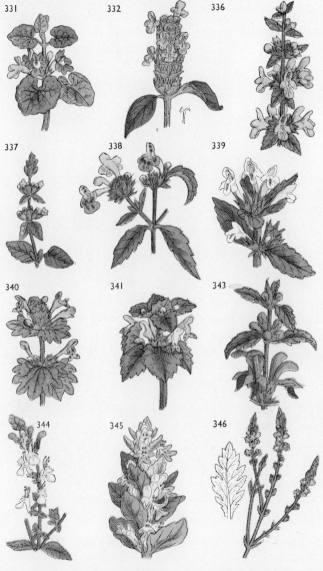

331. GROUND-IVY.
337. FIELD WOUND-
 WORT.
340. HENBIT DEAD-
 NETTLE.
344. WOOD-SAGE.

332. SELF-HEAL.
338. RED HEMP-
 NETTLE.
341. RED DEAD-
 NETTLE.
345. BUGLE.

336. MARSH WOUNDWORT.
339. COMMON HEMP-
 NETTLE.
343. YELLOW ARCH-
 ANGEL.
346. VERVAIN.

Hedgerows, banks, and waste places (Text Fig. 342). The name dead-nettle refers to a certain similarity of appearance to the stinging nettle (No. 379). *Lámium*, of course, never stings.

343. YELLOW ARCHANGEL, WEASEL-SNOUT, *Lámium Galeóbdolon*. Spring to early summer.

A perennial, similar to the last, but usually less densely branched and taller, reaching 2 ft. Hedgerows, woods, and shady places, particularly in the S., but not in Scotland. Name from Greek *lamos*, throat, from the shape of the corolla.

344. WOOD-SAGE, *Teúcrium Scorodónia*. Summer to autumn.

A perennial with a creeping, woody rootstock. Stems hairy, 1 ft. or more high. Leaves downy and wrinkled. Of dry woods and stony hedgerows. Long used in the making of bitter drinks, and at one time in place of hops.

345. BUGLE, *Ájuga réptans, creeping*. Spring to early summer.

A creeping perennial with a tuft of radical leaves, sending out runners which root and develop into new, tufted plants. Flower-stems erect, usually a few inches high, sometimes more. Coloured-foliaged and variegated forms are grown in gardens.

VERVAIN FAMILY, *Verbenáceae*

For the most part a tropical and sub-tropical family of herbs, trees, and shrubs from America, Asia, and Africa, including the teak tree. *Verbéna* is the only British representative, the fruit being a nutlet. The verbena of perfumery is a member of this family though not a true verbena; it is *Líppia citriodoráta, lemon-scented*, from Chile.

346. VERVAIN, *Verbéna officinális, of use to man*. Summer to autumn.

A perennial with stems up to 2 ft. high and straggling wiry branches. Scentless. Of dry waysides and waste places, particularly in the S., not known in Scotland. From ancient times famous as a charm against evil spirits, and also used medicinally, but of no real value. The cultivated verbenas are derived from S. American kinds.

PLUMBAGO or THRIFT FAMILY: *Plumbagináceae*

A small cosmopolitan family with most of its representatives on sea-coasts or in salt places.

Perennial herbs with narrow leaves, usually stiff and mostly radical. Calyx tubular with five lobes. Petals, five. Stamens, five, opposite the petals. Styles, five.

Species of lead-plant (*Plumbágo*) are cultivated.

347. SEA LAVENDER, *Státice Limónium.* Summer to autumn.

Perennial with long radical leaves, growing in a tuft, which narrow to form a stalk. The midrib is very prominent. Flower-stem about 1½ ft. high. Of muddy shores, except in N. or W. Scotland. Selected forms of this and also exotic species are grown in gardens; the flowers are dried for winter decoration.

348. THRIFT, SEA PINK, *Arméria marítima, of the sea.* Summer.

A perennial having a much-branched rootstock. Each branch ends in a tuft of grass-like leaves a few inches long. The leafless flower-stems rise from these, from 3 in. to 9 in. long, carrying a closely clustered head of flowers. Of cliffs and rocky sea-shores, and in a modified form on certain mountains. Long cultivated in selected forms by gardeners.

PLANTAIN FAMILY: *Plantagináceae*

A small family found mostly in the temperate parts of the Old World.

In Britain, herbs with a tuft of radical leaves and a leafless flower-stem ending in a close spike of flowers. The spike and an individual flower are shown in inset, Text Fig. 351. Best known as weeds.

349. GREATER PLANTAIN, *Plantágo májor, greater.* Summer to autumn.

Perennial, with leaves nearly as wide as long, both erect and spreading. Seven, sometimes five or nine, ribs converge into an appreciable stalk. Flower-spike long and slender, very variable in size according to situation. In pastures, waste places, and a weed of cultivation; as such, it has been spread almost all over the world. Once used as a cure for wounds.

350. HOARY or LAMB'S-TONGUE PLANTAIN, *Plantágo média, inter-mediate*. Summer to autumn.

Perennial, the leaves stalkless and spreading on the ground, and downy. Ribs, five or seven. In dry pastures, particularly in lime-stone districts.

351. RIBWORT, *Plantágo lanceoláta, lance-shaped (the leaves)*. Spring to autumn.

Perennial with erect or spreading leaves, narrower than either of the above, with three or five ribs. Sepals marked with a green rib.

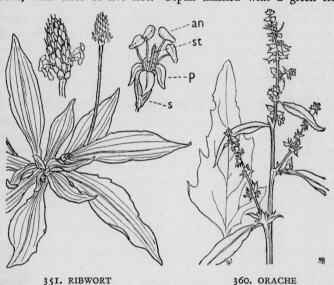

351. RIBWORT   360. ORACHE

Anthers yellow. In fields, pastures, and waste places. Widely spread over the world (Text Fig. 351).

352. SEA PLANTAIN, *Plantágo marítima, of the sea*. Late summer to autumn.

Perennial, with narrow and rather fleshy leaves. Of sea-shores, salt marshes, and mountains.

353. BUCK'S-HORN PLANTAIN, *Plantágo Corónopus*. Summer to autumn.

Annual or biennial, easily identified by its narrow and usually divided leaves. Of poor, dry land, usually near the sea.

KNAWEL or ILLECEBRUM FAMILY: *Illecebráceae*

A small family, with only one common British representative, though one species of *Illecébrum* is found in the extreme S. W.

Usually small annuals or perennials with opposite leaves, sometimes with membranaceous stipules. Flowers very small, greenish. Petals, sepals, and stamens, five; sometimes the petals, always small, are missing.

354. ANNUAL KNAWEL, *Scleránthus ánnuus, annual.* Summer.

Annual, branching from the base, the stems at first spreading. Up to 6 in. high, usually less. Of fields and waste places, abundant locally except in N. Scotland. Name from Greek *skleros*, hard, and *anthos*, flower, referring to the dried appearance of the flower.

GOOSEFOOT FAMILY: *Chenopodiáceae*

A family of herbs and shrubs, with a few small trees, usually associated with the presence of salt in the soil.

Leaves (not always present) usually fleshy, alternate, without stipules. Flowers small, green, consisting of a calyx-like perianth divided into five or fewer segments. Stamens five, opposite the segments. Styles two or three. Fruit a nutlet.

It includes the beetroots, sugar-beet, and mangel-wurzel, derived from species of *Béta* (B. *marítima, of the sea*, is found on our sea-coasts), and spinach, derived from the Mediterranean *Spinácia olerácea, edible*.

355. MARSH SAMPHIRE, GLASSWORT, *Salicórnia herbácea.* Autumn.

A branching annual, with round, succulent stems from 6 in. to $1\frac{1}{2}$ ft. high. The minute flowers form succulent spikes at the tips of the stems. Variable, and often differentiated into several species. Of muddy salt-marshes; it stands submersion by tides. Stems turn red after summer. Name from Latin *sal*, salt, and *cornu*, horn, referring to its home and appearance.

356. SEABLITE, *Suaéda marítima, of the sea.* Summer to autumn.

A branching annual, the stems prostrate, semi-prostrate, or erect, the plant thus varying in height from 2 in. to over 1 ft. Leaves fleshy; the plant sometimes red. Of salt-marshes and sea sands.

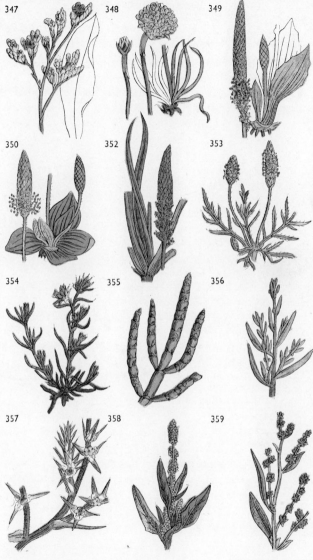

347. SEA LAVENDER.
350. HOARY PLAN-
     TAIN.
354. ANNUAL
     KNAWEL.
357. SALTWORT.

348. THRIFT.
352. SEA PLANTAIN.
355. MARSH SAM-
     PHIRE.
358. WHITE GOOSE-
     FOOT.

349. GREATER PLAN-
     TAIN.
353. BUCK'S-HORN
     PLANTAIN.
356. SEABLITE.
359. SEA PURSLANE.

357. SALTWORT, *Sálsola Káli.* Summer to autumn.

An annual, with spreading stems, about 1 ft. high. Leaves end in a prickle. Of seaside sands and salt-marshes all round Britain. Name from the Latin *sal*, salt.

358. WHITE GOOSEFOOT, FAT HEN, *Chenopódium álbum, white.* Summer to autumn.

An erect annual from 1 ft. to 2 ft. high. Leaves pale green, usually whitish and mealy, particularly on the undersides. Lower leaves stalked, more or less egg-shaped, irregularly toothed. Of cultivated and waste land, particularly rubbish-heaps. There are several other rather similar species, particularly the red goosefoot (*C. rubrum, red*), an erect annual, not mealy, often turning red, and the perennial Good King Henry or allgood (*C. Bónus-Henrícus*), about 1 ft. high, with triangular toothed leaves which are rather thick and dark green, resembling spinach. It was once grown as a vegetable, and is usually found near houses—also called Mercury goosefoot. All these have green flowers. Name from Greek *chen*, goose, and *pous*, foot, from the shape of the lower leaves.

359. SEA PURSLANE, *Átriplex portulacoídes, portulaca-like.* Summer.

A low, spreading, shrubby plant, with silvery foliage, up to 2 ft. high. Leaves entire, mostly opposite. Of sea-shores.

360. ORACHE, *Átriplex pátula, spreading.* Late spring to autumn.

An annual, usually rather spreading, but very variable in growth, up to 3 ft. high. Flowers reddish-green. Of waste places and particularly as a weed of cultivated land (Text Fig. 360). In *Átriplex* the male and female flowers are distinct; the female without sepals, but with two bracts, which usually become thick and warty, closing over the fruits.

BUCKWHEAT OR DOCK FAMILY: *Polygonáceae*

A family consisting in the most part of herbs growing in the N. temperate regions.

Leaves alternate and simple, with a membranous stipule forming a sheath around the stem. Perianth in one piece, with from three to six lobes, green or coloured. Stamens six to nine, styles two or three. Fruit a nutlet, often three-angled.

K

The family includes the Asiatic rhubarbs; *Rhéum officinále, of use to man*, is the medicinal kind, and *R. Rhapónticum* is that used for pies.

361. BROAD-LEAVED DOCK, *Rúmex obtusifólius, broad-leaved*. Summer.

Perennial with a thick rootstock.   Lower leaves heart-shaped, with a rounded top; upper, more lance-shaped.   Flowers green or reddish. The curled dock (*R. críspus, curled*) is a similar plant with narrower leaves which are wavy on the edges.   Both are very common in waste

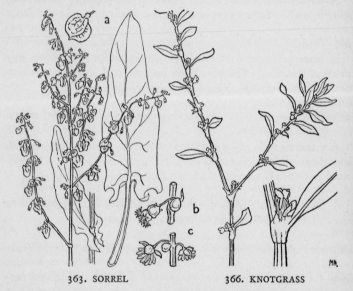

363. SORREL   366. KNOTGRASS

land, as troublesome weeds in pastures, by waysides, and in ditches and hedgerows.

362. WOOD or RED-VEINED DOCK, *Rúmex nemorósus, of woods.*
     Summer.

Similar to the above, but few or no bracts on inflorescence, inner sepals entire.   Leaves sometimes red-veined.   The water dock (*R. Hydrolápathum*) is usually a much larger plant than any of the above, reaching 5 ft., and is found by water-sides and in wet situations.

363. SORREL, *Rúmex Acetósa*.   Summer.

Perennial from 1 ft. to 2 ft. high.   Radical leaves stalked, upper leaves clasping the stem.   The male (*c*) and female (*b*) flowers are normally borne on separate plants; their colour is green or reddish. After fertilization, the segments of the perianth close round the fruit (a) and usually turn red. Of meadows and moist grassland. Sometimes cultivated for its edible leaves, which have an acid flavour (Text Fig. 363).

364. SHEEP'S-SORREL, *Rúmex Acetosélla.* Spring to autumn.

A slender perennial spreading by underground shoots. From 6 in. to 1½ ft. high. Leaves acid, and often turning red. Of dry pastures.

365. MOUNTAIN SORREL, *Oxýria dígyna, with two styles.* Summer.

A perennial about 6 in. high. Leaves mostly radical, flower-stem practically leafless. The leaves have an acid taste. Of mountains in Scotland, N. England, and Wales in damp places.

366. KNOTGRASS, KNOTWEED, *Polýgonum aviculáre, pertaining to birds.* Spring to autumn.

An annual with many wiry branches 1 ft. or more long, usually spreading. Flowers normally pink, but sometimes white. Of cultivated and waste land, particularly as a garden weed (Text Fig. 366).

367. BLACK BINDWEED, CLIMBING BUCKWHEAT, *Polýgonum Convólvulus.* Summer to autumn.

Annual, with a twining or straggling stem, up to 3 ft. long. Of cultivated and waste places; the seed often mixed and spread with grain.

368. AMPHIBIOUS PERSICARY, WATER BISTORT, *Polýgonum amphíbium, amphibious.* Summer.

A perennial, either creeping in damp places, when the stem roots at the joints and the leaves have short stalks and are lance-shaped, or floating in water, when the stems are thicker, the leaves with longer stalks and more heart-shaped. Of water-sides, ponds, and wet places.

369. SPOTTED PERSICARY, *Polýgonum Persicária.* Summer to autumn.

A branching annual up to 2 ft. high, the leaves often turning red. Stipules fringed. Leaves usually marked with a dark spot. Flowers normally pink, but sometimes white or greenish. A variable plant. Of waysides, waste, and cultivated places. Pale persicary (*P. lapathifólium, dock-leaved*) is a very similar plant; it has pale green unspotted leaves, stipules without a fringe, and greenish flowers.

370. Waterpepper, *Polýgonum Hydropíper.* Summer to autumn.

An annual very similar to spotted persicary, but more slender; the stems incline to a creeping habit, and if chewed the plant has a biting taste. In wet ditches and by water-sides.

Bistort or snake weed (*P. Bistórta*), a perennial from 1 ft. to 2 ft. high, with pink or sometimes white flowers and heart-shaped leaves on long winged stalks, is found in damp meadows and shady places

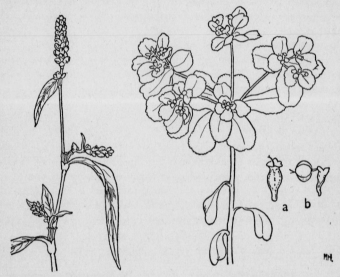

369. SPOTTED PERSICARY   372. SUN SPURGE

in the N. The handsome Japanese knotweed (*P. cuspidátum, having leaves with a sharp tip*), a vigorous plant about 5 ft. or 6 ft. high, spreads rapidly and is difficult to eradicate when once established. It is often found in dense patches near gardens. Other kinds are cultivated, and nearly all are inclined to be invasive.

DAPHNE FAMILY: *Thymelaeáceae*

Only represented in Britain by *Dáphne*, this family is found particularly in S. Africa and Australia.

Usually shrubs, often with stringy bark. Leaves alternate without stipules. Flower without petals, the green or coloured sepals being united to a long tube. In Britain, fruit a berry.

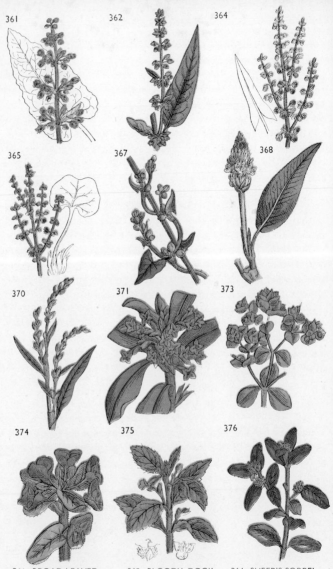

361. BROAD-LEAVED
DOCK.
365. MOUNTAIN SORREL.
370. WATERPEPPER.
374. WOOD SPURGE.

362. BLOODY DOCK.
367. BLACK BIND-
WEED.
371. SPURGE LAUREL.
375. DOG'S MERCURY.

364. SHEEP'S-SORREL.
368. AMPHIBIOUS
PERSICARY.
373. PETTY SPURGE.
376. BOX.

371. SPURGE LAUREL, *Dáphne Lauréola*. Spring.

An erect evergreen shrub from 2 ft. to 4 ft. high, with shiny green leaves, green, scentless flowers, and black, acrid, poisonous berries. Of moist, shady places, usually woods in the S. Rare in Scotland and not found in Ireland. The mezereon (*D. Mezéreum*) is claimed as a British native; it is seldom found except in gardens, where, in early spring, before its leaves open, it bears sweetly scented pink (sometimes white) flowers. Berries red, poisonous. The bark and berries of both daphnes have been used as purgative medicines, but they are extremely poisonous.

SPURGE FAMILY: *Euphorbiáceae*

One of the largest families, with some 4,000 species, mostly tropical shrubs and trees, though including succulent plants and herbs.

The family has various kinds of foliage and inflorescence, but the flowers are always unisexual. The ovary nearly always consists of two or three carpels. In the fruit they separate from each other, each usually with one seed, which is often ejected explosively.

The British species are all herbs. The castor-oil plant (*Rícinus commúnis, common*) is sometimes cultivated decoratively in Britain in several varieties. It is grown in warm climates, particularly India, for the seeds (which are ejected violently when ripe, and are very poisonous), from which castor oil, valuable as a lubricant and medicine, is expressed.

372. SUN SPURGE, *Euphórbia Helioscópia*. Summer to autumn.

An erect annual, from 6 in. to 1 ft. or more high. The 'flower' (*a*) is really an inflorescence; a cup, appearing to be the corolla, is actually a series of joined bracts. At its base are enclosed ten or more stamens, each one being a separate male flower. The female flower with its stigma is on a short stalk in the centre. After fertilization this stalk lengthens, and the fruit projects beyond the remains of the cup (*b*). These inflorescences are borne on a five-rayed umbel. Juice milky, poisonous. Distinguished by its toothed leaves. The fruit is used by ants, who help to distribute the seed. Of waste and cultivated land (Text Fig. 372).

373. PETTY SPURGE, *Euphórbia Péplus*. Summer to autumn.

An annual, much branched, from 6 in. to 1 ft. high, the flowering umbels with two or three rays usually forming most of the plant. Inflorescence as No. 372 but cup has long points to its teeth. Juice milky, poisonous. Leaves entire. Of waste land and gardens.

374. WOOD SPURGE, *Euphórbia amygdaloídes, almond-like.* Spring.

Perennial with a woody rootstock and several erect, stout, and un-branched stems, often red-coloured. Inflorescences as No. 372 but with longer teeth to the cup. Juice milky, poisonous. Of woods and hedgerows, common except in N. England, rare in Ireland; not found in Scotland.

Euphórbia is a large genus, with about 750 species, varying from the British herbaceous species to leafless desert succulents. Its dis-tinguishing feature is the poisonous milky juice, bitter and purgative. *E. pulchérrima*, from Mexico, is the greenhouse poinsettia.

375. DOG'S MERCURY, *Mercuriális perénnis, perennial.* Early spring.

A perennial with a creeping rootstock, and erect, simple stems, about 9 in. high. Flowers before the leaves are fully open, male and female on separate plants. It has an unpleasant smell and although poisonous was once popular as a medicine. Drying reduces the poisonous properties. Of woods, hedgerows, and shady places. The god Mercury is said to have discovered its medicinal virtues.

BOX FAMILY: *Buxáceae*

A small family distinguished from the spurges chiefly by the absence of milky juices, but otherwise rather similar and formerly included in *Euphorbiáceae*. It consists of evergreen shrubs.

376. BOX, *Búxus sempervírens, evergreen.* Spring.

An evergreen shrub or occasionally a small tree, usually wider than its height. Male and female flowers separate but in the same cluster. Fruit a capsule. Probably native in S. England, but for the most part originally planted. Used for topiary work (see No. 1). The timber is white and hard with a very close, even grain; it was used for wood engraving and is still valued for rules, handles of tools, etc., though now mostly imported.

CROWBERRY FAMILY: *Empetráceae*

A small family of heath-like plants found in the N. hemisphere and the Andes. The leaves are incurved and filled with hairs. The following is the only British representative.

377. CROWBERRY, *Empétrum nígrum, black.* Spring.

A low, spreading, evergreen shrub, heath-like in appearance, the branches rooting. Leaves with their edges rolled back. Male and female flowers on separate plants. Fruit berry-like; sometimes eaten. Of moorlands, particularly in Scotland, Ireland, and the N. Name from Greek *en*, on, *petra*, rock, the plant often growing in stony places.

WATER-STARWORT FAMILY: *Callitrichaceae*

A small family of floating water plants with minute flowers, rather similar to the mare's-tail family (*Haloragidaceae*, page 70) and often included with it.

378. WATER-STARWORT, *Callítriche aquática, of water.* Summer to autumn.

A rather small aquatic perennial or sometimes annual. In water, the upper leaves float in a star-like rosette on the surface, the submerged leaves being much narrower. In wet mud it becomes a creeping plant, rooting as it goes. The minute male and female flowers are separate, but on the same plant. Of shallow waters and mud. Name from Greek *kalos*, beautiful, and *thrix*, hair, referring to the growth, or perhaps to the leaves, of certain species.

NETTLE FAMILY: *Urticáceae*

A family of herbs and undershrubs found both in tropical and temperate regions.

Leaves opposite or alternate, usually hairy and with stipules. Flowers small, male and female separate, sepals, joined, four or five, petals missing. Fruit a nutlet.

Distinguished from the elm family principally by differences in the inflorescence, and from the mulberry family by the presence of latex in the latter.

379. STINGING NETTLE, *Urtíca dioíca, dioecious.* Summer to autumn.

Perennial with a vigorous creeping rootstock and erect stems from 2 ft. to 3 ft. or more high. The lower leaves somewhat heart-shaped, the upper more lance-shaped. The whole plant covered with both down and stinging bristles. Male and female flowers normally on separate plants. Of hedgerows, waysides, waste, and cultivated places. The small nettle (*U. úrens, stinging*) is an annual, smaller than the last, about 1 ft. high only. The male and female flowers are mixed in small clusters. Name from Latin *uro*, literally, *I burn*.

380. PELLITORY-OF-THE-WALL, *Parietária officinális, of use to man.* Summer to autumn.

A perennial, branching from the base and usually spreading. Stems reddish, up to 1 ft. or more long. Male and female flowers mostly separate. On old walls and in stony places, rare in the N. Name from Latin *paries*, a wall.

MULBERRY FAMILY: *Moráceae*

A family consisting chiefly of shrubs and trees, but including some herbs and climbers, generally tropical or sub-tropical.

Features somewhat variable, but most have leaves with stipules, male and female flowers separate, and contain latex. A number are aromatic and include resins.

It is economically a useful family, including the common mulberry (*Mórus nígra, black*), which probably originated in Persia, and has been grown in Britain for three centuries or more; the Asiatic white mulberry (*M. álba, white*) on which silk-worms are fed, seldom seen in Britain; hemp (*Cannábis satíva, cultivated*), probably of Asiatic origin, cultivated for its fibres used in rope-making, and which, only when cultivated in hot countries, produces also an intoxicating resin; the fig (*Fícus cárica, of Caria in S.-W. Asia Minor*), long cultivated in the Mediterranean district but probably originating in W. Asia; and the hops.

381. HOP, *Húmulus Lúpulus.* Summer.

A perennial with long left-hand twining stems which climb through hedgerows and small trees. Male flowers small and in a panicle; female enclosed by a 'cone' of scales, which, when they enlarge after fertilization, provide (from cultivated forms) the brewer's hops. In this state the scales of the hop enclose the small fruit, and bear resinous glands which contain the bitter aromatic substance lupulin. The plant is native of S. Britain, but is generally found as an escape from cultivation. The decorative hop, *H. japónica, Japanese*, is grown in gardens; it is not aromatic.

ELM FAMILY: *Ulmáceae*

A family of deciduous trees found in both tropical and temperate regions. Closely allied to the nettle family, in which it is sometimes included.

Leaves alternate and undivided, with stipules that soon fall. Calyx bell/shaped without petals. Fruit a one/seeded nutlet surrounded by a wing.

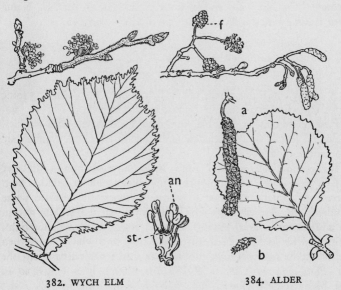

382. WYCH ELM   384. ALDER

382. WYCH or SCOTCH ELM, *Úlmus glábra, smooth*. Early spring.

A large spreading deciduous tree, forming a short, thick trunk with a large open head of branches. Young shoots downy and buds hairy. Flowers crimson, in dense stalkless clusters. The fruit is flat and oval, with the seed in the centre. The tree does not sucker. Native of N. Britain (Text Fig. 382). The English or common elm (*U. procéra, tall*) is a big, upright tree with a tall, straight trunk, and long ascending branches. The leaf and flower are not dissimilar to the wych elm. It seldom develops from seed, but produces suckers freely, from which it is propagated. It is native of S. Britain. A fungus disease, first reported in 1928, has caused havoc with trees of this species; it has been suggested, however, that some trees are immune and that the epidemic will die down. Branches sometimes snap off without warning in calm weather. The stems were once hollowed out and used as water-pipes. The timber of both trees is tough, useful, and very durable providing that it is kept permanently either dry or wet—alternating conditions rot it. It is used for packing-case ends, boxes, coffins, and under-water woodwork. Other species, varieties (such as the weeping wych elm), and hybrids are grown in Britain.

BOG-MYRTLE FAMILY: *Myricáceae*

Only genus, *Myríca* consisting of temperate and sub-tropical shrubs, with alternate undivided leaves. Male and female flowers separate in catkins. Fruit usually a nut. Many are aromatic.

Closely related is the walnut family (*Juglandáceae*). It includes the American hickories and the common walnut tree (*Júglans régia, royal*), an E. European and Asiatic tree which has been cultivated in Britain for centuries. The leaves have five or more oval, pointed leaflets, and are aromatic when rubbed. Their edges are not cut. The flowers are in catkins, the male about 3 in. long. The fruit is green and smooth, enclosing the walnut of dessert.

383. SWEET GALE, BOG MYRTLE, *Myríca Gále*. Early spring.

A deciduous shrub about 3 ft. high, spreading by suckers. Leaves and stems fragrant. Male and female flowers normally on separate plants, opening before the leaves. Of damp moors, particularly in the N.

BIRCH FAMILY: *Betuláceae*

A small family of deciduous trees and shrubs growing in the N. temperate regions or on mountains in the tropics. Often very abundant.

Leaves undivided, stipules falling early. Male and female flowers, separate on the same plant, in catkins which are formed during the summer before they flower. Fruit a nutlet.

384. ALDER, *Álnus glutinósa, sticky*. Early spring.

A deciduous, narrowly pyramidal tree, not of great height. Young shoots slightly sticky. Male flowers in long catkins, reddish when open (*a*); female flowers small (*b*). Fruiting catkin egg shaped, remaining on the tree long after the fruit has fallen (*f*). Of water sides and boggy places. The timber is light in weight, and used for artificial limbs, rollers, clogs, and similar purposes (Text Fig. 384).

385. WHITE BIRCH, *Bétula pubéscens, slightly downy*. Spring.

A small or occasionally middle sized deciduous tree of rather upright growth. Bark white, peeling off in papery layers, the stem becoming darker with age. Young twigs downy, without warts. It is often confused with the silver birch (*B. verrucósa, warty*), usually a larger tree, with pendulous branches, and the young twigs not downy but bearing small warts. The two grow together abundantly on heaths, moors, mountain sides, and in pine and oak woods. They also hybridize and produce intermediate forms. The timber is used for furniture and turnery, but mostly imported. The dwarf birch (*B. nána, dwarf*) is a small shrub, of wet places in mountains of the N. The sap of birches is very free flowing; birch oil is obtained from a N. American species.

386. HORNBEAM, *Carpínus Bétulus*. Spring.

A medium sized deciduous tree, rounded when mature. The stem is ridged or fluted. The fruiting catkins have prominent three lobed bracts, which remain around the fruit. The tree is often confused with the beech, but easily identified by the furrowed stem. The timber is very hard, and is used for small parts such as piano parts and cogs.

387. HAZEL or COBNUT, *Córylus Avellána*. Late winter.

A large bushy shrub or occasionally small tree, suckering from the base. Young twigs downy. Female flowers like leaf buds, but with the crimson stigma protruding. Male flowers in catkins, yellow. Nuts in a leafy husk with lobed edges, never longer than the nut. Of hedgerows and copses—a British native, unlike the filbert (*C. máxima, largest*) which is a S. European plant, and the parent of the cultivated filberts. It is easily distinguished by the narrower nut, completely enclosed by the husk, which usually projects beyond it.

BEECH FAMILY: *Fagáceae*

Mostly trees, widely spread over the world, represented by *Nothofágus* in the S. hemisphere, species of which are now cultivated in Britain.

Leaves alternate, evergreen (in exotic species) or deciduous. Stipules scaly, falling as the leaves open. Male and female flowers separate on the same tree, in catkins, the male usually large. Fruit a nut held in a cup.

388. COMMON OAK, *Quércus pedunculáta, stalked.* Spring.

A rugged, gnarled, spreading tree. Leaves stalkless or with a short stalk, acorns one or more clustered at the end of a thin stalk. The other

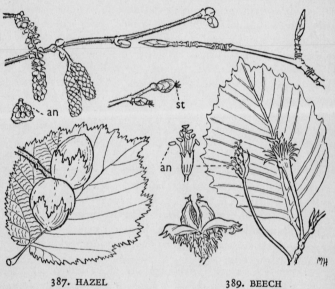

387. HAZEL   389. BEECH

British oak is the durmast oak (*Q. sessiliflora, with sessile flowers*). This is a more erect tree, with leaves on a stalk, and the acorns in clusters close to the twig, practically without stalk. In both, the female flowers are small, the male in long catkins; they open with the leaves. Oaks are the largest and longest-lived trees in Britain; their timber is valuable and used for numerous purposes. The evergreen or holm oak (*Q. Ilex*) is a Mediterranean tree which has been grown in Britain for over three centuries. Several N. American kinds are also found in parks, etc.

389. BEECH, *Fágus sylvática, of woods.* Spring.

A tall deciduous tree, with a smooth, grey, straight trunk. Flowers

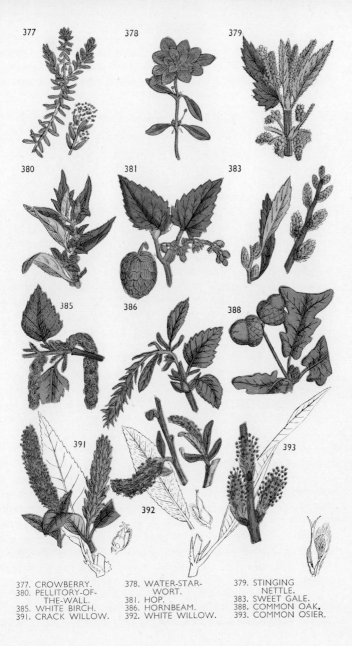

377. CROWBERRY.
380. PELLITORY-OF-
     THE-WALL.
385. WHITE BIRCH.
391. CRACK WILLOW.

378. WATER-STAR-
     WORT.
381. HOP.
386. HORNBEAM.
392. WHITE WILLOW.

379. STINGING
     NETTLE.
383. SWEET GALE.
388. COMMON OAK.
393. COMMON OSIER.

only every few years, the male and female flowers separate, on the same tree, the female being globular. Fruit, two or three nuts ('mast') enclosed in a prickly case, which splits open when ripe. The leaves are very densely arranged, and allow little to grow under the tree. The timber is cheap and much used for many purposes, such as furniture, wooden parts of tools, and turned articles (Text Fig. 389). The copper beech is a variety.

390. SWEET or SPANISH CHESTNUT, *Castánea satíva, cultivated*. Summer.

A very large and handsome deciduous tree, though often grown as a coppice (i.e. cut back periodically to provide numerous long thin poles). Male flowers long yellow catkins, female flowers often found at the base of the male. Fruit, two or three nuts enclosed in a very prickly case which splits open when ripe; seldom eaten from British trees, but on the Continent numerous select forms are cultivated widely for the fruit. The coppice wood is used for poles and fencing; the mature timber is also split and used for fencing, as well as for gate-posts, carriage builders' frames, and cabinet making (Text Fig. 390). No relative of horse-chestnut (No. 84).

WILLOW FAMILY: *Salicáceae*

A family of trees and shrubs including only the willows and poplars, found in the N. temperate, tropical, and sub-tropical zones.

Leaves alternate, undivided, the stipules falling early. Male and female flowers, in catkins, on separate plants. Fruit a capsule, the seed bearing long silky hairs, usually viable only for a very short period. Hybrids frequently occur. Many species sucker freely.

391. CRACK WILLOW, *Sálix frágilis, brittle*. Spring.

A large tree with a bushy head and rough corrugated bark. The twigs branch off at a wide angle; when bent, they snap off very easily at a joint. Of stream-sides and moist places. For timber, see below.

392. WHITE WILLOW, *Sálix álba, white*. Spring.

A tall deciduous tree, the branches somewhat weeping at the ends. The twigs branch off at a much narrower angle than the last, and the leaves, usually pale green, are covered on the underside with a silvery down. The cricket-bat or blue willow (*S. coerúlea, blue*) is a hybrid between the last two; the branches are erect, and the leaves lose their down, becoming blue underneath. Of stream-sides and in moist places. The timber is used for the best cricket-bats, while that of the previous two is used for cheap bats, and where a tough wood which withstands friction is required, such as in cart bottoms. Willow is also used for chip baskets and hurdles.

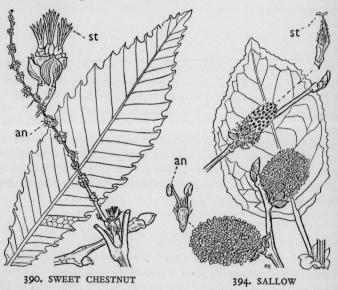

390. SWEET CHESTNUT   394. SALLOW

393. COMMON OSIER, *Sálix viminális, with long, flexible shoots.* Early spring.

An erect deciduous shrub or small tree with straight and slender branches. Leaves long and slender, very silvery underneath. Flowers before the leaves open. Of water-sides and moist places. Extensively cultivated in several varieties for basket-making.

394. SALLOW, GOAT WILLOW, PALM, *Sálix Capréa.* Early spring.

A deciduous shrub or small tree. The grey-green leaves are wrinkled and variable in shape; sometimes the base is heart-shaped. The stipules are broad. The young shoots are at first downy. The yellow male flowers are often open at Easter and called 'palm' for that reason. Of hedgerows and open places (Text Fig. 394). The same

English names are often applied to at least two other species: the grey willow (*S. cineréa, ash-grey*) which has smaller leaves and catkins, and which is covered with a grey down that lasts longer than on *S. Capréa*, and the round-eared willow (*S. auríta, with ears*). This is smaller than *S. Capréa*, both in height, leaf, and size of catkin, and the leaves are more wrinkled. All occupy similar situations. They seed more freely than the other willows, and numerous intermediate hybrids are said to occur.

395. CREEPING WILLOW, *Sálix répens, creeping*. Spring.

A low, straggling, deciduous shrub, creeping extensively underground, about 1 ft. high. Young shoots and underside of leaves silky. In summer the plants often seem to be covered with cotton wool, in reality the silky fruit. Of damp moors, heaths, and sandy soils. In garden soil, this shrub will reach 6 ft. The weeping willow (*S. baby-lónica, Babylonian*) is a native of China. Although probably introduced to N. Europe from the Euphrates, where it has long been cultivated, it is not the willow of 'the rivers of Babylon' mentioned in the Bible—this was a poplar. There are numerous species of willow, including intermediate forms difficult to name, but those mentioned above are perhaps the most usually encountered and recognized.

396. ASPEN, *Pópulus trémula, quaking*. Early spring.

A small tree or sometimes a large bush. The grey-green leaves are woolly when young; they have a two-edged compressed stalk, and quiver in the slightest breeze. Catkins grey with purple stigmas. Of woods and copses, particularly in the N., where it is native. Timber used for matches (Text Fig. 396). The grey poplar (*P. canéscens, greyish*) is a tall tree with yellowish-grey bark, and a furrowed stem when mature. The leaves are more or less heart-shaped, with a few large rounded teeth, and often downy on the undersides of the leaves at the ends of the shoots. The tree suckers very freely. It is native of S. Britain, and is often wrongly called the abele or white poplar, which is a much rarer tree, with whiter and downier palmately-lobed leaves, and not native. The Italian black poplar (*P. serótina, later in the year*) is frequently planted. It is a remarkably quick-growing tree with a tall, straight trunk (often leaning away from the prevailing wind) and rather few but long branches. A continental hybrid, it is always male, and owes its specific name to the late season at which the leaves open—so escaping damage from late spring frosts. Also called the Canadian

poplar.   The Lombardy poplar (*P. nígra* var. *itálica, black, Italian variety*)
is a tall, extremely narrow tree, with all its branches erect. It was brough
from Italy in the eighteenth century, and is extensively planted.   Popla
timber is tough, not easily splintered, and non-inflammable.   It is
therefore, used for cart-bottoms, floors, brake-blocks, and other work
required to stand rough usage.

II*b*. MONOCOTYLEDONS

Seeds with one seed-leaf or cotyledon.   Stems without definite pith,
wood, and bark, but consisting of bundles of fibres surrounded by

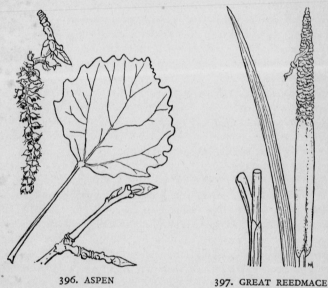

396. ASPEN   397. GREAT REEDMACE

tissue, which, in woody kinds, is enclosed by a hard adherent skin.
Leaves usually simple and entire, with simple parallel veins, their bases
often forming a sheath around the stem or next leaf.   The parts of the
flowers most frequently in threes.   The calyx and corolla are often
similar, forming a perianth of six segments, three inner and three outer.

REEDMACE FAMILY: *Typháceae*

A small family of aquatic herbs.   Male and female flowers separate on
the same plant, in spikes or clusters, without perianth.   Fruit a small nut.

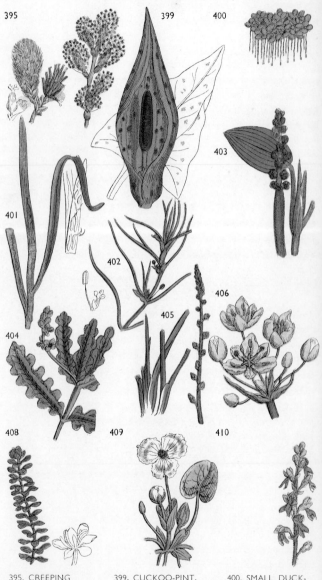

397. GREAT REEDMACE, CAT'S TAIL, *Týpha latifólia, broad leaved*. Summer.

Perennial with somewhat creeping rootstock. Stems reed like, up to 6 ft. long. Leaves long and narrow, sheathing the stem. Flower spike sometimes a foot long, the upper part consisting of the yellow anthers, the lower of the ovaries covered with dense brown hairs. Often wrongly called bulrush (see No. 439) (Text Fig. 397). The lesser reedmace (*T. ángustifólia, narrow leaved*) is somewhat smaller, and has a space of bare stem between the male and female flowers. Both are water side or ditch plants. Name from Greek *tuphos*, a fen, from its situation.

BUR REED FAMILY: *Sparganiáceae*

A small family of aquatic plants limited to *Spargánium*, which is distributed in the cool and temperate regions of both hemispheres. Very similar to the last family.

398. BRANCHED BUR REED, *Spargánium eréctum, upright*. Summer.

Perennial with erect, branching stems from 2 ft. to 3 ft. long. Leaves strap like, long and narrow. Flowers at top of stem, male in small clusters (green till pollen is liberated, then yellow), above the green female flowers in larger clusters. Of water sides (Text Fig. 398). The simple bur reed (*S. símplex, simple*) is smaller, with fewer flower heads, the female being separate on short stalks. Name from Greek *sparganon*, a band, from the shape of the leaf.

ARUM FAMILY: *Aráceae*

A large family, for the most part confined to tropical and warm climates, very variable in habit and foliage. The flowers are closely packed in a dense spike, called a *spadix*, which is surrounded by a large sheathing bract called a *spathe*. Fruit a berry.

399. CUCKOO PINT, WAKE ROBIN, LORDS AND LADIES, *Árum maculátum, spotted*. Spring.

Perennial, the rootstock being an acrid white tuber, once used for making starch. Spathe 6 in. or more long. Berries red, after the leaves and spathe are dead. The plant has an unpleasant smell, and is poisonous, particularly the berries. Of woods and hedgerows.

L

DUCKWEED FAMILY: *Lemnáceae*

A family restricted in Britain to the duckweeds (*Lémna*) which are small floating water plants without true stems or leaves, but consisting of fronds, usually with small fibrous roots from their under-surface. The flower, seldom produced, is enclosed in a minute spathe, and appears from an opening in the frond. The plants increase by new fronds growing from the edges of the old ones; these eventually become detached. In autumn special buds form which sink to the bottom of the water and hibernate till spring when they rise to the surface and develop. *Wólffia arrhíza, rootless,* a member of this family rarely found in Britain, has the distinction of being the smallest flowering plant.

400. SMALL DUCKWEED, *Lémna mínor, smaller.* Summer.

Frond about ¼ in. long, egg-shaped, the top bright green. Root single. Flowering patches distinguished by their yellowish colour; it flowers more freely than the other three British species.

PONDWEED FAMILY: *Potamogetonáceae*

A family of aquatic plants found over the world in fresh and salt water, having creeping rootstocks and long, branched stems. Flowers small and green, without or with a perianth of four segments. Fruit, seed-like nuts.

401. GRASS-WRACK, *Zostéra marína, of the sea.* Summer.

Perennial, rootstock and stems rooting in the mud, rather fleshy. Leaves narrow and about 3 ft. long. Of muddy coasts, growing near low-water mark. It is often thrown up by storms. The flowers are pollinated under water. Favourite food of wild ducks, geese, and swans. Name from Greek *zoster,* a riband, from the leaf.

402. HORNED PONDWEED, *Zannichéllia palústris, of swamps.* Summer.

Stem floating, and branched. Leaves bright green. Male and female flowers separate in the axils of the leaves, without perianth. Of ponds, ditches, and brackish water. Named after a Venetian botanist, Zannichelli.

403. BROAD-LEAVED PONDWEED, *Potamogéton nátans, floating.* Summer.

Perennial, the upper leaves floating on the surface. The submerged leaves narrower. Flowers in a short spike held above water. In most types of fresh water—still, running, deep, shallow, etc., and varying accordingly in growth.

404. CURLY PONDWEED, *Potamogéton críspus, curled.* Summer.

Leaves all submerged, thin, narrow, up to 2 in. long, and wavy on the edges. Of ponds and streams. The opposite-leaved pondweed (*P. dénsus, dense*) has many small leaves, all submerged, opposite, in two

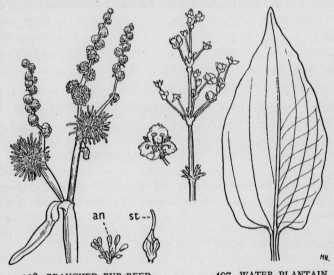

an   st--

398. BRANCHED BUR-REED   407. WATER PLANTAIN

rows on opposite sides of the stem. Fennel pondweed (*P. pectinátus, comb-like*) has much-branched slender stems and narrow leaves, giving the appearance of an under-water fennel; it usually grows densely. There are several other species, often, however, difficult to differentiate. Name from Greek *potamos*, river, and *geiton*, neighbour, on account of their situation.

SCHEUCHZERIA FAMILY: *Scheuchzeriáceae*

A small family of perennial herbs of grass-like habit. One species of *Scheuchzéria* is a very rare British plant; it owes its unfortunate name to the Scheuchzers, Swiss botanists, born in the eighteenth century.

405. MARSH ARROW-GRASS, *Triglóchin palústre, of marshes.* Summer.

A suckering, tufted perennial with slender, juicy leaves about 6 in. long. Flower-stem up to 1 ft. Of marshes, wet heaths, and meadows. A seaside and salt-marsh form, with fleshier leaves, is the sea arrow-grass (*T. marítimum, of the sea*). Name from Greek *treis*, three, *glochin*, point, from the bristles on the carpels. Fruit a seed-like nut.

WATER PLANTAIN FAMILY: *Alismáceae*

A small family of marsh and water plants found in most parts of the world. Flowers usually coloured and often large, in terminal umbels, panicles, or racemes, with a perianth of either six similar segments, or three sepal-like and three petal-like. The genus *Bútomus* is now usually placed in a family of its own, *Butomáceae*.

406. FLOWERING RUSH, *Bútomus umbellátus, umbellate.* Summer.

A perennial with a thick, creeping rootstock. Leaves long, sedge-like, triangular, broadened at the base. Flower-stem leafless, sometimes 4 ft. long but usually less. Ditches and still, shallow water.

407. WATER PLANTAIN, *Alisma Plantágo-aquática.* Summer.

Perennial, rootstock much thickened by the sheathing bases of the leaves. Flower-stem up to 3 ft. long, with whorls of unequal branches carrying the small rose-coloured flowers on whorled stalks. Of streams and water-sides (Text Fig. 407).

FROG-BIT FAMILY: *Hydrocharidáceae*

A small family of water plants widely spread over the world. Male and female flowers usually on separate plants, the buds enclosed by from one to three membraneous bracts. Sepals three, united. Petals three, united. The small green fruit ripens under water, and the seeds are liberated when it rots.

408. AMERICAN WATER-WEED, WATER-THYME, *Elódea canadénsis, Canadian.* Summer to autumn.

A much-branched perennial, forming dense, submerged masses. Flowers in the upper leaf axils, the males (very rare) floating to the surface, where they burst and distribute pollen to the female flowers, which reach the surface by means of a long perianth tube. Of ditches

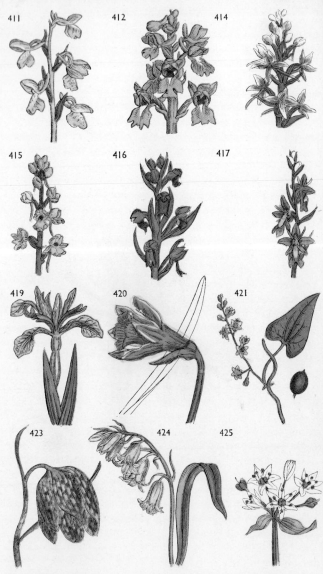

411. GREEN-WINGED
    ORCHIS.
415. FRAGRANT ORCHID.
419. GLADDON.
423. SNAKE'S-HEAD.

412. EARLY PURPLE
    ORCHIS.
416. FROG ORCHID.
420. DAFFODIL.
424. BLUEBELL.

414. BUTTERFLY
    ORCHID.
417. FLY ORCHID.
421. BLACK BRYONY.
425. RAMSONS.

and still water. Native of N. America, it was introduced about a century ago, and has now spread throughout Britain. Name from Greek *helos*, marsh, from its situation.

409. FROGBIT, *Hydrócharis Mórsus-ránae*. Summer.

Stems form long floating runners which bear rosettes of leaves floating on the surface of the water, and tufts of submerged roots. Male flowers held above water on stalks, in twos or threes, female sessile among the leaves. Autumn buds are formed which sink; in spring these rise and form rosettes, from which the runners are produced. Of ponds and ditches. Name from Greek *hudor*, water, and *charis*, beauty.

The water-soldier (*Stratiótes aloídes, aloe-like*) has flowers similar to the last, but a rootstock creeping in the mud with long, narrow, fleshy leaves edged with pointed teeth. Found particularly in the fens.

ORCHID FAMILY: *Orchidáceae*

A large family of perennial herbs, with some 7,500 recognized species, found particularly in the tropics, but spreading even to the arctic regions. The tropical kinds (which include most of the species and florists' hybrids grown in greenhouses) frequently live on trees in forests, without being in any way parasitical. Most orchids found in temperate climates, and all in Europe, are, however, 'terrestrial,' i.e. grow in the ground. They usually have thick, fleshy roots.

The distinguishing feature of the family is that the stamens and style are never separate, but fused together in a column (see page 10 and Plate III). The pollen is usually sticky, and never dusty. The fruit is a capsule which splits open, liberating innumerable seeds like sawdust. Leaves simple, with parallel veins, and sheathing the stem.

The species of British orchids are quite numerous, but most are rather uncommon, and nearly all kinds are local in their distribution. It is now known that they normally grow, and that the seeds germinate, in the presence of particular fungii. All kinds are often indiscriminately called *Órchis*; while all are orchids, the name *Órchis* belongs to one genus alone.

410. TWAYBLADE, *Lístera ováta, egg-shaped* (the leaves). Summer.

Stem 1 ft. or often more high, without any leaves from the base, but bearing normally two opposite leaves about 6 in. from the ground. Of woods, shady places, and moist pastures, particularly in the N.

The lesser twayblade (*L. cordáta, with heart-shaped leaves*) is a similar but much smaller plant about 6 in. high. Named after Dr. Martin Lister, a seventeenth-century traveller and naturalist.

411. GREEN-WINGED ORCHIS, *Órchis Mório.* Early summer.

With two entire globular tubers. Stems variable in height, but about 6 in. Leaves few, narrow, and strap-shaped. Of moist meadows and open woodland. Abundant locally in S. Britain and Ireland.

412. EARLY PURPLE ORCHIS, *Órchis máscula, masculine.* Spring to early summer.

With two entire tubers, egg-shaped. From 6 in. to 1½ ft. high. Leaves broad with blunt ends, often spotted. Open woods, moist meadows, and shady places, often growing with cowslips. Has several local names.

413. SPOTTED ORCHIS, *Órchis maculáta, spotted.* Spring to early summer.

Tubers rather flat with several finger-like lobes. Stem about 1 ft. high. Leaves usually marked with dark spots. Flowers pale pink marked with a deeper shade, but very variable in colour and in the shape of the lip. One of the commonest orchids, of copses, pastures, field-sides, and similar situations, not usually in very wet ground (Text Fig. 413). Name from Greek *orchis*, testicle, alluding to the two tubers.

414. BUTTERFLY ORCHID, *Habenária bifólia, two-leaved.* Summer.

Tubers entire, oval. Stem up to 1½ ft. high, with two large leaves at its base. Flowers sweet-scented. Of damp places such as heaths, pastures, and marshes. Also called *Platánthera.*

415. FRAGRANT ORCHID, *Habenária conópsea, cone-like (the inflorescence).* Summer.

Tubers palmate. Leaves narrow and pointed. Stem from 6 in. to 1½ ft. high. Sweet-scented. Of grassy places, chalk downs, and banks, mostly on limy soils. Particularly in Ireland and Scotland. Also called *Gymnadénia.*

416. FROG ORCHID, *Habenária víride, green.* Summer.

Tubers lobed. Stems about 6 in. high. Leaves few, oblong or

lance-shaped. Of grassy land, especially on hillsides and downs with limy soil in N. England, Scotland, and Ireland. Also called *Coeloglóssum*.

417. FLY ORCHID, *Óphrys muscífera, moss-like*. Spring to early summer.

Tubers entire. Stem slender, from 4 in. to 1 ft. high, with only three or four flowers, which are remarkably like insects. Leaves fairly

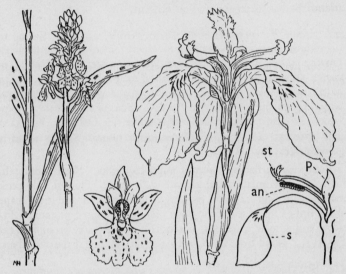

413. SPOTTED ORCHIS   418. YELLOW FLAG

narrow and pointed. Of open woods, clearings, and chalk downs, mostly in E. and S.-E. England, not found in Scotland. The bee orchid (*O. apífera, with bee-like flowers*) is a larger plant with a few rather large flowers having broad lips coloured a rich velvety brown, found on dry limy pastures, in the same districts as the last. Name from Greek *ophrus*, eyebrow, from the markings on the lip.

IRIS FAMILY: *Iridáceae*

A large family, with most members in S. Africa and tropical America.

Perennials, with tuberous, creeping, or bulbous rootstocks. Flower with six petal-like segments, three stamens, and one style divided into three stigmas. Fruit a three-chambered capsule.

In gardens, the *Gladíolus* from the Cape of Good Hope and its hybrids are generally grown (the genus includes a few European species also), as well as the less popular *Íxia* and *Tigrídia* from the same country, and the American *Sisyrínchium*. But most frequently seen is the crocus, cultivated here for centuries and now often more or less naturalized. It is an extensive genus, found particularly in Spain, around the Mediterranean, and in W. Asia.

418. YELLOW FLAG, *Íris Pseudácorus*. Summer.

Perennial with a thick creeping rootstock. Stem 2 ft. or more high. Flowers yellow, in twos or threes enclosed by a sheathing bract. The showy 'falls' are the equivalent of sepals; the petals are small and more or less erect, while the fringed, crest-like appendages end in the stigmas, which are on the lower side at the tips. They arch over the anthers, which are coated with pollen on the under side (see inset, Fig. 418). This structure may be followed out in the numerous irises found in gardens (Text Fig. 418).

419. GLADDON, STINKING IRIS, ROAST-BEEF PLANT, *Íris foetidíssima, very fetid*. Early summer.

Perennial with a branching rootstock. Stems up to 2 ft. high, leaves taller and evergreen; when crushed, they have a strong smell. Seeds bright orange or scarlet. Of woods and shady places on limy soils, particularly in the S. Name from Greek *íris*, rainbow, alluding to the colours of the flowers.

Many species, varieties, and hybrids of iris are cultivated in gardens, all from the N. temperate regions. They are of two distinct kinds, those with creeping rootstocks or rhizomes, and those with roots springing from bulbs. The fragrant orris root is the dried rhizome of the Florentine iris.

AMARYLLIS FAMILY: *Amaryllidáceae*

A large family, for the most part centred in dry tropical or sub-tropical countries, but with several temperate representatives. Root-stock generally bulbous, from which spring the parallel-veined leaves. The flower consists of six petal-like segments, with six stamens (distinguishing it from the iris family). The ovary is always below (i.e. nearer the root than) the other parts of the flower.

Several greenhouse plants, such as the *Amaryllis* from Cape Colony and *Hippeástrum* from tropical and sub-tropical America, are among its members. The snowdrop (*Galánthus nivál15, of snow*) is well known and widely naturalized in Britain, but is not considered a true native.

420. DAFFODIL, LENT LILY, *Narcíssus Pseúdo-narcíssus*. Early spring.

A bulbous perennial, with two or three bluish-green leaves up to 1 ft. long. Flower-stem usually somewhat taller than the leaves bearing a solitary scentless flower. Of open woods and meadows, not native in Scotland or Ireland. The specific name meaning 'false narcissus' is an ancient one, now misleading and senseless. The cultivated daffodil, originating from the numerous species found chiefly in S. Europe, S.-W. Asia, and the Mediterranean regions. Though sold under the different names of daffodil and narcissus, there is, of course, no valid difference between the two, one being the English, the other the Latin name for the flower.

YAM FAMILY: *Dioscoreáceae*

A family of tropical and warm temperate districts, usually climbing herbs or shrubs, with tuberous or thick woody rootstocks. Leaves alternate, netted between the veins. Male and female flowers separate on the same plant. Perianth segments six, all like petals. Fruit a capsule or berry.

Limited in Britain to one species. The yams, whose tuberous roots replace the potato in some tropical countries, particularly S. America, are species of *Dioscórea*.

421. BLACK BRYONY, *Támus commúnis, common*. Spring to early summer.

Perennial with a tuberous rootstock, stems twining through hedges and trees. Leaves sometimes three-lobed. Male flowers in long, slender racemes, female in short racemes. Berries scarlet, usually conspicuous and numerous. Of hedgerows and open places in woods, in England and Ireland, but not Scotland. No relative of the true bryony (No. 146). The tubers and berries are poisonous.

LILY FAMILY: *Liliáceae*

One of the largest families with some 3,700 species mostly found in tropical and warm climates. It consists of herbs, shrubs, and some

trees. The rootstock is usually creeping or bulbous. The flower
generally has six petal-like segments, six stamens, and a single style
sometimes divided into three. The perianth and stamens are always
attached below the ovary. Fruit a capsule or berry.

The family is of little importance economically, though it includes
the onions (*Állium*) and asparagus (*Aspáragus officinális, of use to man*), a
coastal plant sometimes found wild on the W. and S.-W. shores of
Britain. But it contains many of the most beautiful garden flowers,
including the lilies (*Lílium*) themselves, none native, but many of which
thrive in Britain. Popular kinds range from the old Madonna (*L.
candídum, pure white*) and martagon (*L. Mártagon*) lilies, introduced from
C. and E. Europe in the sixteenth century or before, to the handsome
Lilium regále, royal, brought from W. China in 1905. The family includes the tulips from S. Europe and W. Asia, though the fragrant
yellow *Túlipa sylvéstris, wild*, is claimed as a rare native; the florist's
hyacinths, varieties of *Hyacínthus orientális, eastern*, from the Levant; the
common dog's-tooth violet (*Erythrónium Dens-cánis*) from Europe; and
the shrubby yuccas from N. and C. America. All these have been
cultivated for centuries. The aspidistra (*A. lúrida, dingy*), a native of
China and Japan, was introduced in 1822. British natives, but best
known as garden plants, are Solomon's seal (*Polygonátum*) and lily-
of-the-valley (*Convallária majális, of May*).

422. BUTCHER'S BROOM, *Rúscus aculeátus, prickly*. Spring.

A dark-green plant of a shrub-like evergreen habit, 2 ft. or more
high. Rootstock creeping. The 'leaves' are really flattened stems,
which bear the flowers. These are small and whitish-coloured, the
male and female on separate plants. The berries are red. Of woods
and shady places under trees, particularly in the S. Once used to make
brooms for cleaning butcher's blocks (Text Fig. 422).

423. SNAKE'S-HEAD, FRITILLARY, *Fritillária Meleágris*. Late spring.

A bulbous plant with few narrow leaves. Of moist meadows, now
rather rare, but often artificially naturalized around gardens. Name
from Latin *fritillus*, dice-box, from the shape (some say marking) of
the flower.

424. BLUEBELL, *Scílla nonscrípta*. Spring.

A bulbous plant with thick drooping leaves. Flower-stem about
1 ft. high bearing the flowers in a terminal one-sided drooping raceme.

Of woods and shady places. The bluebell of Scotland is the English
hare-bell (No. 259). The spring squill (*S. vérna, of spring*) is a small
plant, the stem about 6 in. high carrying upright blue flowers, not
common, but where found (usually near the coast in pastures) abundant.

425. RAMSONS, *Állium ursínum, of bears.* Spring to early summer.

A bulbous herb, with broad, flat, spreading leaves, and a flower-stem
about 9 in. high carrying a loose umbel of flowers. Smells of onion.

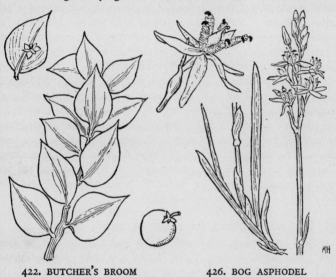

422. BUTCHER'S BROOM   426. BOG ASPHODEL

The onion, leek, garlic, and chive are all cultivated species of *Allium*
from Europe and N. Asia.

426. BOG ASPHODEL, *Narthécium ossifrágum.* Summer.

Perennial with creeping rootstock. Stem 6 in. to 1 ft. carrying deep
yellow flowers in a terminal raceme; the stems turn a reddish-brown.
The stamens are covered with wool. Of bogs and wet moors (Text
Fig. 426).

427. MEADOW SAFFRON, *Cólchicum autumnále, autumn.* Autumn.

A bulbous perennial. The flowers, appearing before the leaves, are
like a crocus, but have six stamens instead of three. The leaves are
produced in spring; they are about 9 in. long and 1 in. wide, and are

particularly poisonous to stock, both fresh and dried in hay. They cause violent purging. Of moist meadows in England, rare in Ireland, and not native in Scotland. The seeds and corm contain the same alkaloid poison as the leaves; from them a drug, valuable in gout, is prepared. The plant is often wrongly called autumn crocus, a name which belongs to the numerous crocus proper (not native, but often cultivated) which flower in autumn. Saffron is not prepared from colchicum, but from the saffron crocus (*C. sativa, cultivated*). Named after Kolchis, in Asia Minor, famous in ancient times for its drugs and sorcery.

RUSH FAMILY: *Juncáceae*

A herbaceous family with comparatively few species which are, however, very abundant in damp places all over the world, from the arctic to the tropic regions.

Rootstock usually creeping. Leaves cylindrical or grass-like. Flowers small, usually wind-fertilized, consisting of six dry sepal-like segments. Stamens six or three. Style with three stigmas. (See insets, Text Figs. 428 and 434.) Fruit a capsule. All the following kinds are abundant in Britain.

428. COMMON RUSH, *Júncus commúnis, common*. Summer.

A perennial with matted, creeping rootstock. Stems up to 3 ft. long, cylindrical, with solid pith, pliable and leafless, in thick tufts. Certain of these bear the greenish or brown flowers in dense clusters about 6 in. from the top. The stems are sheathed at the base in brown scales, and were once used for wicks. Of wet and marshy places. Sometimes divided into two distinct species, *J. effúsus, spreading loosely*, and *J. conglomerátus, clustered*. (Text Fig. 428.)

429. JOINTED RUSH, *Júncus articulátus, jointed*. Summer.

Perennial with branching rootstock. Flowering stems slender, up to 2 ft. high. Leaves stem-like, the pith intermittent, giving them the appearance of being jointed, particularly when dried. Moist places.

430. HEATH RUSH, MOSS RUSH, *Júncus squarrósus, rough*. Summer.

Perennial, with dense tufts of narrow, grooved, spreading leaves, about 6 in. long. Flower-stem up to 1 ft. high. Of heaths and moors, turning brown in autumn.

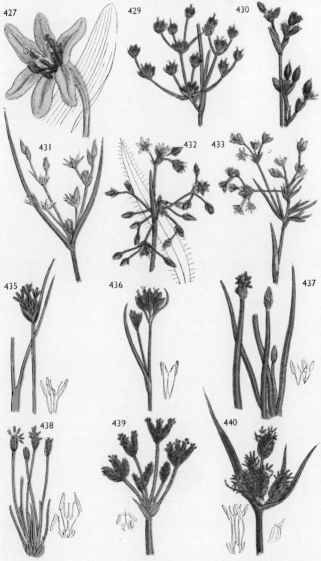

427. MEADOW SAF-
    FRON.
431. TOAD RUSH.
435. BOG-RUSH.
438. DEER'S GRASS.

429. JOINTED RUSH.
432. HAIRY WOODRUSH.
436. WHITE BEAK-
    SEDGE.
439. BULRUSH.

430. HEATH RUSH.
433. GREAT WOODRUSH.
437. MARSH OR CREEP-
    ING CLUB-RUSH.
440. SEA CLUB - RUSH.

431. TOAD RUSH, *Júncus bufónius, toad-like.* Summer.

A slender branching annual, up to 6 in. or so high, but often much ess. Leaves short and slender. Of wet places. Name from Latin *ungo,* I join, from the use of the stems for tying bundles.

432. HAIRY WOODRUSH, *Lúzula pilósa, with scattered soft hairs.* Spring.

Perennial with creeping stock. Leaves a few inches long, soft and rass-like. Flower-stems erect, up to 1 ft. high. Flowers usually

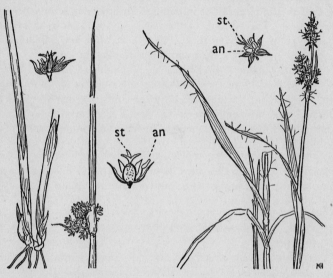

428. COMMON RUSH   **434. FIELD WOODRUSH**

eparate. Variable, and often divided into distinct species. Of voods, banks, and shady pastures.

33. GREAT WOODRUSH, *Lúzula sylvática, of woods.* Early summer.

Perennial, much larger than the other British woodrushes. Stems ft. or more long. Leaves about ¼ in. wide and 1 ft. long. In open voods.

34. FIELD WOODRUSH, *Lúzula campéstris, of plains.* Spring.

Perennial with a creeping rootstock, flowering stems and leaves a tufts. Flowers brown, in clusters; this differentiates it from the hairy voodrush. Of dry pastures, woods, and heaths (Text Fig. 434).

SEDGE FAMILY: *Cyperáceae*

A large and widely distributed family, with some 2,700 species, consisting chiefly of marsh plants, frequently perennials with creeping rootstocks. The appearance is often grass-like. Flower-stems usually three-angled and solid, surrounded by sheathing leaves which are not split. Flowers minute, greenish or brownish, each in the axil of a small bract, arranged in small spikes or 'spikelets.' The spikelets are solitary and terminal, or in terminal clusters, spikes, or other inflorescences. The perianth of the flower, if any, consists of bristles or small scales. Stamens three. Fruit a seed-like nut. Pollination by wind. In *Cárex* the male and female flowers are separate.

Of little economic or ornamental use, though papyrus, used before paper, was made from *Cypérus Papýrus* which grows in warm countries. In Britain, the presence of sedges indicates that the land is damp. There are numerous species, often difficult even for an expert to distinguish, but the following are amongst the commonest.

435. Bog-rush, *Schoénus nígricans, becoming black*. Summer.

Perennial with rush-like stems about 1 ft. high and short leaves with dark sheaths, growing in close tufts. Spikelets almost black. Of bogs and marshes, usually near the sea.

436. White Beak-sedge, *Rhynchóspora álba, white*. Summer to autumn.

Perennial without creeping rootstock. Stems forming grass-like tufts, about ¾ ft. high. Leaves short. Spikelets almost white. Of bogs. Name from Greek *runchos*, beak, and *spora*, seed.

437. Marsh or Creeping Club-rush, *Scírpus palústris, of marshes*. Summer.

Rootstock branching and creeping vigorously, sending up tufts of flowering stems between 6 in. and 1 ft. high. Leaves reduced to scale sheaths around the bases of the stems. Of bogs and water-sides.

438. Deer's Grass, Tufted Scirpus, *Scírpus caespitósus, of tufted growth*. Summer.

Rootstock branched, with close tufts of wiry green stems up to 1 ft. high, the leaves in the form of sheaths with narrow leafy tips. Of moorlands, particularly in the N.

39. BULRUSH, GREAT CLUB-RUSH, *Scírpus lacústris, of lakes.*
Summer.

Rootstock creeping. Stems erect, a foot or two or even 8 ft. high,
circular at the base, which bears a short leaf, more or less triangular at
the top. Barren leafy tufts are found floating in the water. Of water-
sides and watery ditches.

40. SEA CLUB-RUSH, *Scírpus marítimus, of the sea.* Summer.

Perennial with creeping rootstock. Stems up to 5 ft. high, triangular. Leaves flat and pointed, often longer than the stems. Of
marshes and estuaries near the sea.

41. COTTON-GRASS, *Erióphorum angustifólium, narrow-leaved.* Summer.

Perennial with creeping rootstock. Stems about 1 ft. high, triangular. Flowers brown, surmounted by cottony bristles, which
develop considerably with the fruit. Of wet moors, heaths, and bogs.
There are one or two very similar species. Name from Greek *erion*,
wool, and *pherein*, to bear, alluding to the fruits. (Text Fig. 441.)

42. STAR-HEADED SEDGE, *Cárex echináta, prickly.* Spring to early
summer.

Perennial, tufted, with stems about 6 in. high. Leaves shorter than
the stem. Fruits with a long beak, spreading. Marshes.

43. REMOTE-FLOWERED SEDGE, *Cárex remóta, scattered.* Early
summer.

Perennial with slender stems from 1 ft. to 1½ ft. high, with long
leafy bracts. Spikelets far apart. Of moist, shady places and woods.

44. SAND or SEA SEDGE, *Cárex arenária, of sandy places.* Summer.

Perennial with a rootstock which creeps extensively, sending up
many shoots, from a few inches to 1½ ft. Stem rough, three-angled.
Leaves stiff and rough. Of sandy places around the coast, where the
matted rootstocks help to bind the sand together.

45. COMMON or TUFTED SEDGE, *Cárex Goodenóvii.* Spring to
summer.

Perennial with a creeping rootstock and stiff, slender stem from 1 ft.
to 1½ ft. high. Leaves narrow. Very common in pastures, meadows,
and marshes. There are other very similar closely allied species.

446. ROUND-HEADED SEDGE, *Cárex pilulífera, pill-headed.* Early summer.

Perennial with stems 6 in. to 1 ft. high, forming tufts. Leaves shorter than the stem, weak. Of heaths and moors.

447. DISTANT-SPIKED SEDGE, *Cárex dístans, distant.* Early summer.

Perennial with tufted stems 1 ft. to 2 ft. high with long sheaths.

441. COTTON-GRASS   451. SWEET-SCENTED VERNAL-GRASS

Leaves shorter than the stem. With few spikelets, far apart. Of marshes and wet moors. There are several similar and closely allied species.

448. CARNATION SEDGE, CARNATION-GRASS, *Cárex panícea, like Panicum (panic grass).* Early summer.

Perennial with spreading rootstock and tufts of short blue-green leaves and three-angled arching stems, from 1 ft. to 1½ ft. high. Of meadows and moist places.

449. WOOD SEDGE, *Cárex sylvática, of woods.* Early summer.

Perennial with weak, arching, three-angled, leafy stems, from 1 ft to 2 ft. high. Leaves and leafy bracts long and limp. Of woods and shady places except in N. Scotland.

Of some forty other species of *Cárex,* the pendulous sedge (*C. pendula, drooping*), with stout triangular stems up to 5 ft. high with long broad leaves and drooping spikelets, is both striking and common.

GRASS FAMILY: *Gramíneae*

One of the largest families of flowering plants with some 450 genera and 4,500 species, extending from the extreme limits of flowering plants at the poles and on mountain-tops to the equator. It is of extreme importance to man, providing his cereals and other food and much of the pasturage for his cattle and stock. It includes the bamboo, almost tree-like in some species, perhaps now not so important as in earlier civilizations, but still of great use.

In Britain the family consists of herbs, mostly perennial but some annual. The rootstocks are often running or creeping. The leaves alternate in two opposite rows, the stem swollen and jointed where they arise. The leaf forms a sheath, often split on the side opposite the blade, surrounding the stem. Where it joins the blade there is a small scale called the *ligule*. The flower-stem is hollow except at the joints, and is generally known as the *culm*. The flower is described on page 10 and Plate III. It is pollinated by wind. The fruit is seed-like and called a *grain*, often enclosed by remains of the flower which when separated is called the *chaff*. There are some 150 British species, with very numerous varieties and hybrids, many difficult to identify, but those given below include the commonest and best known.

The family includes: maize (*Zéa Mays*), an important cereal in the New World; rice (*Orýza satíva, cultivated*), a swamp plant cultivated in the warm parts of Asia, Africa, and Australia; and the sugar-cane (*Sacchárum officinárum, of use to man*) grown in the W. Indies. In Britain, rye (not very frequently), wheat, barley (see No. 468), and oats (see No. 463) are grown. Rye (*Secále cereále, grain-bearing*) is an introduced plant; it is not much grown in this country for bread-making (as it is on the Continent, particularly in cold places on account of its hardiness) but for green fodder. Cultivated wheat is also not native; it consists of very distinct races of *Tríticum vulgáre, common*. All have close, spike-like heads, but some are 'bearded,' bearing long bristles on the glumes, while others are not. The grain is of two colours, white

M

or red. Towards harvest-time a field of wheat is golden or red-gold, of oats a paler yellow, and of barley, silver-coloured. The origins and early cultivation of these and other *Gramineae* are obscure and take us back to the early civilizations; but it may be mentioned that seeds found (reputedly) in mummies and old tombs have, when sown, grown into kinds only produced during recent years by modern hybridists.

450. SPREADING MILLET-GRASS, *Mílium effúsum, spreading.* Early summer.

A creeping perennial with culms from 3 ft. to 4 ft. Leaf-blades broad and flat, glossy light green. Of moist woods. *Mílium* is the Latin name for millet, here misapplied. The millet long cultivated for its grain in S. Europe, Egypt, and Asia is *Pánicum miliáceum, millet-like.*

451. SWEET-SCENTED VERNAL-GRASS, *Anthoxánthum odorátum, sweet-scented.* Late spring.

A small tufted perennial with culms up to 1½ ft. but often less. Leaves hairy in varying degree. Flowers yellowish. The plant is sweetly scented, particularly when drying. An important and hardy constituent of grassland and pastures, but not valuable as a grazing or hay plant. Name from Greek *anthos*, flower, and *xanthos*, yellow (Text Fig. 451).

452. REED CANARY-GRASS, *Phálaris arundinácea, rush-like.* Summer.

A creeping, semi-aquatic perennial. Culms up to 5 ft. high, with numerous spikelets in a panicle. Of water-sides and marshes, the matted rootstocks making it a preventive of fresh-water erosion. A garden form is the variegated 'gardener's garters.'

453. CAT'S-TAIL, TIMOTHY, *Phléum praténse, of meadows.* Summer.

A variable tufted perennial, with soft, light-green leaves. Culm from 1½ ft. to 2 ft. high. Flower 'spikes' about 2 in. long, often longer. Introduced to the U.S.A. about 1720 by Timothy Hansen, it was later reintroduced to Britain in a somewhat different cultivated form. Of meadows and pastures, selected forms being good for hay and grazing.

454. MEADOW FOXTAIL, *Alopecúrus praténsis, of meadows.* Spring to early summer.

A tufty perennial with smooth, dark-green foliage. Culms between 1 ft. and 3 ft. high, flower 'spikes' usually not so long as the last.

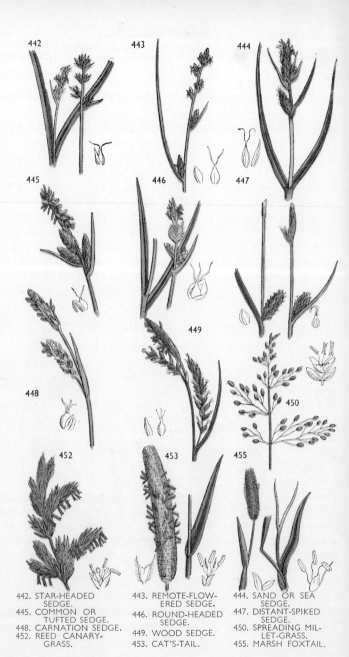

442. STAR-HEADED
    SEDGE.
445. COMMON OR
    TUFTED SEDGE.
448. CARNATION SEDGE.
452. REED CANARY-
    GRASS.

443. REMOTE-FLOW-
    ERED SEDGE.
446. ROUND-HEADED
    SEDGE.
449. WOOD SEDGE.
453. CAT'S-TAIL.

444. SAND OR SEA
    SEDGE.
447. DISTANT-SPIKED
    SEDGE.
450. SPREADING MIL-
    LET-GRASS.
455. MARSH FOXTAIL.

Of moist or rich meadows and pastures.   One of the most valuable
hay and grazing grasses (Text Fig. 454).

455. MARSH or FLOATING FOXTAIL, *Alopecúrus geniculátus, with
knee-like joints.*   Early summer.

A semi-aquatic perennial, the culms 1 ft. to 1½ ft. long, bending
like knees at the joints.   Moist meadows and marshes.

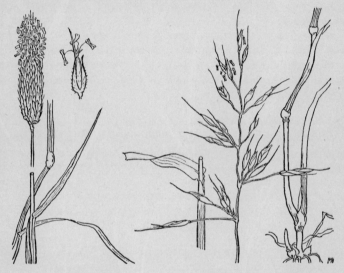

454. MEADOW FOXTAIL   **464. FALSE-OAT GRASS**

456. MARSH BENT-GRASS, *Agróstis palústris, of marshes.*   Late
summer.

A semi-aquatic perennial producing runners which root when in
contact with the wet soil.   Leaves rather dense, narrow, and finely
pointed.   Culms 2 ft. or more high.   Of water-sides and land liable
to flood.   The creeping bent-grass is a similar though less vigorous
plant of damp meadows.   Both of these are often regarded as one of
several varieties of the white bent (*A. álba, white*), another of which is
the cultivated fiorin grass.

457. BROWN BENT-GRASS, *Agróstis canína, dog.*   Summer.

Perennial, creeping along the surface and rooting at the joints.
Lower leaves very fine and needle-like, upper flatter but still narrow.

Culms 1 ft. to 2 ft. high. Of damp meadows and heaths. Valuable in lawns.

458. MARRAM-GRASS, SEA MAT-GRASS, *Psámma arenária, of sandy places.* Summer.

Perennial with a vigorous, creeping rootstock which serves to bind the sand of sea-coasts, where it abounds. Leaf erect, long and narrow, ending in a sharp point. Culms about 2 ft. high. Name from Greek *psammos*, sand.

459. TUFTED HAIR-GRASS, *Aíra caespitósa, tufted.* Summer.

Perennial, growing in large dense tufts. Leaves narrow, rolled in dry weather, dark green. Variable in height, culms from 1½ ft. to 3 ft. or even more. Moist shady places.

460. WAVY HAIR-GRASS, *Aíra flexuósa, with zig-zag stems.* Summer.

A tufted perennial, smaller than the last, with narrow leaves rolled so that they appear solid, dark green. Culms 1 ft. to 1½ ft. high. Of heaths and upland pastures.

461. EARLY HAIR-GRASS, *Aíra praécox, early.* Spring.

An annual, densely tufted, with short fine leaves. From 3 in. to 6 in. high. Of sandy and upland pastures.

462. SILVER HAIR-GRASS, *Aíra caryophýllea, clove-coloured.* Early summer.

A slender tufted annual, much the same as the last, but with a spreading panicle. Of sandy and upland pastures.

463. WILD OAT, *Avéna fátua, barren. Summer.*

An erect, slender annual. Leaf-blades broad, pointed. Flowers in a large spreading panicle. Culms 3 ft. to 5 ft. high. A common weed of cereal crops, rather variable in its habit. Yellow oat-grass (*A. flavéscens, yellowish*) is a smaller plant than the above, perennial and tufted, between 1 ft. and 2 ft. high. Panicles also smaller, golden-yellow. Of dry meadows and pastures, not common in Scotland or Ireland. The cultivated oat, of which there are two distinct strains each including several varieties, is of obscure origin. It is easily distinguished in growth by its spreading panicle of flowers. The grain is long and narrow, and is used for flour in northern countries, but mostly for feeding stock. A cool, moist climate produces the best quality.

464. FALSE-OAT GRASS, *Arrhenátherum avenáceum, oat-like*. Summer.

An erect perennial, growing in loose tufts with few leaves, having a bitter taste. Culms from 2 ft. to 4 ft. high, flower-panicles large, slightly drooping to one side. Of hedgerows and in meadows, where, growing with other grasses, it is valuable for pasture and hay. Some-times, particularly in a bulbous-rooted form called 'onion couch,' a troublesome weed (Text Fig. 464 and Plate III).

465. YORKSHIRE FOG, MEADOW SOFT-GRASS, *Hólcus lanátus, woolly*. Summer.

A tufted perennial covered with soft hairs, giving the plant a soft feel. Leaves pale grey-green. The veins of the basal sheaths are pink. Culms from 1 ft. to 2 ft. high. Very abundant as a weed in meadows and pastures, particularly in moist soils.

466. MOOR MAT-GRASS, *Nárdus stricta, upright*. Summer.

A small densely tufted perennial, with fine, wiry, erect leaves, very stiff and bristle-like. Culms about 6 in. high. Of moors, heaths, and hill pasture. Name from Greek *nardos,* spikenard (*Nárdostachys, Valerian family*), from some resemblance.

467. MEADOW BARLEY-GRASS, *Hórdeum praténse, of meadows*. Summer.

A tufted perennial. Leaf-blades hairy above, glossy below, pale green, narrow and pointed. Culms from 1½ ft. to 2 ft. high. Of meadows when damp or on heavy soils. Rare in Ireland and Scotland.

468. WALL BARLEY-GRASS, *Hórdeum murínum, mouse-like*. Early summer.

A tufted annual. Foliage light green, hairy on both sides. Culms 1 ft. to 2 ft. high. Of roadsides and waste places. Rare in Ireland and Scotland.

Cultivated barley (*Hórdeum satívum, cultivated*) is said to be derived from a W. Asian species. The ears are spike-like, consisting of numerous groups of three-flowered spikelets. The three important races grown have respectively six rows, apparently four rows, or two rows of grain, running up and down the 'spike.' Most kinds bear long bristles on the flowers, and are called *bearded*; beardless varieties are, however, grown. Barley is primarily used for malting.

469. COUCH-GRASS, *Agropýron répens, creeping.* Summer.

A perennial with an extensive and vigorously creeping rootstock, each piece of which will, if broken off to include a joint, form a new plant. Leaf-blade long and narrow, tapering at each end, pointed at the apex. Culms from 1 ft. to 2 ft. or more high. An abundant and troublesome weed on cultivated ground, being the true 'squitch' or 'twitch,' a name applied (with its local variations) to other grasses of a weedy, running habit.

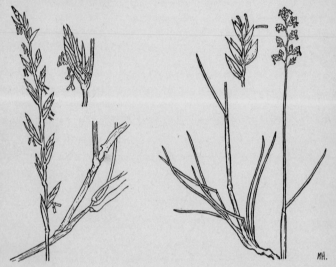

470. PERENNIAL RYE-GRASS   475. SHEEP'S FESCUE

470. PERENNIAL RYE-GRASS, *Lólium perénne, perennial.* Early summer.

A tufted perennial. Leaf-blades dark green, smooth and glossy below, dull above. The lower sheaths are pink or red near the ground. Culms 1 ft. to 2 ft. high. Of meadows, pastures, and waste places; a valuable grazing plant. Darnel (*L. temuléntum, nodding*), an annual found as a cornfield weed, abundant as such in Asia Minor and Syria, is said to be the tare of the Bible.

471. WOOD FALSE BROME-GRASS, *Brachypódium sylváticum, of woods.* Summer.

A tufted perennial, erect, with long, drooping, pale green foliage. Culms about 2 ft. high. Of woods, hedgerows, and shady places.

456. MARSH BENT-GRASS.
459. TUFTED HAIR-GRASS.
462. SILVER HAIR-GRASS.
466. MOOR MAT-GRASS.

457. BROWN BENT-GRASS.
460. WAVY HAIR-GRASS.
463. WILD OAT.
467. MEADOW BAR-LEY-GRASS.

458. MARRAM-GRASS.
461. EARLY HAIR-GRASS.
465. YORKSHIRE FOG.
468. WALL BARLEY-GRASS.

Name from Greek *brachys*, short, and *podion*, a foot, from the short stalks to the spikelets.

472. WOOD or HAIRY BROME-GRASS, *Brómus ásper, rough*. Summer.

A tufted biennial or perennial. Leaves have long blades, tapered at each end, drooping, with long hairs on their sheaths. Culms from 3 ft. to 6 ft. high. Of hedgerows, woodsides, and similar shady places.

473. BARREN BROME-GRASS, *Brómus stérilis, barren*. Late spring to early summer.

An erect annual or biennial, leaf-blades and sheaths rather downy. Culms 1 ft. or 2 ft. high. Waste places and waysides, usually in moist situations.

474. FIELD BROME-GRASS, *Brómus arvénsis, of cultivated fields*. Early summer.

An erect annual or biennial. Leaf-blades thin and sharply pointed. Panicle open and somewhat drooping, but not so much as in the last. Culms from 1 ft. to 3 ft. high with large joints. Soft brome-grass (*B. móllis, soft*) is a very similar plant, the panicles being closer and more upright. Of meadows, cultivated and waste places. There are other species closely allied and similar to these two. *Bromus* is the Greek name for the oat.

475. SHEEP'S FESCUE, *Festúca ovína, sought by sheep*. Early summer.

A close, tufted perennial, with narrow leaves permanently folded. The sheaths of the radical leaves are deeply split. Culms about 6 in. high. At high elevations the flowers form buds with rudimentary roots. On falling they develop into new plants. Very variable, with several marked varieties. Of mountain and dry, poor pastures. Red fescue (*F. rúbra, red*) is similar in appearance and situation; it is a con-stituent of the famous Cumberland turf. Varieties of both are used for lawns (Text Fig. 475).

476. TALL FESCUE, *Festúca elátior, taller*. Summer.

A coarsely tufted perennial. Leaf-blades flat, dark green, ribbed and rough on the upper surface, smooth and glossy under. Culms 3 ft. to 5 ft. high. Of meadows and pastures, particularly where moist. Meadow fescue, often regarded as a different form of this, is very similar, but smaller and more refined in all its parts, the culms reaching from

1½ ft. to 2 ft. high. Both are useful hay and grazing grasses under suitable conditions. Name from Latin *festuca*, a stem.

477. COCK'S⁄FOOT, *Dáctylis glomeráta, clustered.* Late spring onwards.

A coarse perennial forming dense tufts. Foliage dull, variable in colour, but usually rough and somewhat drooping. Culms 2 ft. to 3 ft. Abundant in many types of situation. Name from Greek *dactylos*, a finger, from the shape of the opening inflorescence (Text Fig. 477).

478. CRESTED DOG'S⁄TAIL, *Cynosúrus cristátus, crested.* Summer.

Perennial, tufted, with short, narrow, dark⁄green leaf⁄blades. Culms wiry from 9 in. to 1½ ft. high; often rejected by sheep in pastures, and by mowing machines on lawns and greens, they are known as 'bents.' Valuable for grazing, particularly in dry hill pastures and downs, where it is frequent. Also used for lawns, etc. Name from Greek *kuon*, dog, and *oura*, tail, alluding to the inflorescence.

479. QUAKING⁄GRASS, *Bríza média, intermediate.* Early summer.

An erect perennial, tufted or slightly creeping, the culms from 1 ft. to 1½ ft. high bearing the spikelets on fine pendulous stems. Of moors, meadows, and pastures, particularly on poor soils.

480. REED MEADOW⁄ or SWEET⁄GRASS, *Glycéria aquática, of water.* Summer.

A large reed⁄like perennial with stems creeping and rooting at the joints. Leaf⁄blades 1 in. or so wide, containing air cavities. Culms 3 ft. to 6 ft. high. The plant is harsh to the touch. Of water⁄sides. Less common in Scotland than in England or Ireland. Floating sweet⁄grass, flote⁄grass, or manna⁄grass (*G. flúitans, floating*) is a creeping perennial of wet ditches and still water⁄sides, with soft, thin leaf⁄blades often floating on the water, supported by air cavities, and culms from 1½ ft. to 2 ft. high; it will grow in drier situations. Both provide grazing in undrained fields. Name from Greek *glykeros*, sweet.

481. ANNUAL MEADOW⁄GRASS, *Póa ánnua, annual.* Most of the year.

A tufted annual with flat, weak, and often puckered leaf⁄blades, bright green. Culms from an inch or two to 1 ft. high. Found almost all over the world, particularly as a weed of cultivation and in waste places. The common grass weed found in paths. Of no value in pastures.

482. SMOOTH-STALKED MEADOW-GRASS, *Póa praténsis, of meadows.*
Early summer.

A creeping perennial with dark-green narrow leaf-blades. Culms between 1 ft. and 2 ft. high. A variable species, abundant in meadows, pastures, and waysides; a tough plant useful in pastures and playing-fields. *P. trivialis, common,* does not creep and has roughish stalks.

483. WOOD MEADOW-GRASS, *Póa nemorális, of woods.* Summer.

A tufted or slightly creeping perennial of delicate habit with dark-green narrow foliage. Culms slender, from 1½ ft. to 2 ft. high. Of

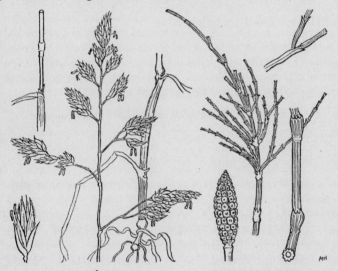

477. COCK'S-FOOT   486. FIELD HORSETAIL

woods and moist shady places. Sea poa (*P. marítima, of the sea*) is a common shore-plant. It is a creeping perennial with short, narrow leaf-blades which are often rolled up. Name from Greek *poa,* fodder.

484. PURPLE MELICK-GRASS, FLYING BENT, *Mólinia caérulea, blue.*
Late summer and autumn.

A coarse upright perennial, tufted. Leaves chiefly from the base, blades long, flat, stiff, and tapering from the middle to a long point. Culms up to 3 ft. high, the lower sections swollen and used as food stores. Of wet moors, peaty soils, woods, and waste places. Of little value, often destroyed by cultivation. Named after a Chilean author and naturalist Molina (1740–1829). The true melicks are *Mélica*; wood melick (*M. uniflóra, one-flowered*) is a slender perennial from 1 ft. to 2 ft. high with a sparsely branched panicle with few spikelets, the flowers brown or purple, found in woods and shady places, and flowering in early summer.

485. COMMON REED, *Arúndo Phragmítes*. Summer to autumn.

A creeping, aquatic perennial. Leaves long, all along the stem, about 1 in. wide. Culms from 5 ft. to 8 ft. high or even more. Found from the tropic to the arctic zones. Of marshes, water-sides, shallow water, and similar situations.

CHAPTER V

FLOWERLESS PLANTS—CRYPTOGAMS

PLANTS without perianth, stamens, pistil, seed, or indeed any of the floral parts normally found in the kinds previously described. They are mostly reproduced by minute *spores*, often microscopically small, contained in *spore-cases* or *sporangia*. The development from spore to plant is quite unlike that of seed to plant; in the case of the fern spore, it is outlined below.

The *Cryptogams* include such plants, often minutely small, as mosses, lichens, fungi, selaginellas, clubmosses, and algae. For the most part, their study and identification is difficult, needing the use of microscopy; consequently, they are not here included. On the other hand, ferns and horsetails have much more in common, particularly in the popular mind, with flowering plants, and so their common kinds are the only *Cryptogams* illustrated and described in this book.

HORSETAIL FAMILY: *Equisetáceae*

A family living mostly in the temperate and cold parts of the N. hemisphere, often found in a fossilized state, but now only represented by *Equisétum*, consisting of leafless herbs, usually with creeping root-stocks. They are rich in silica, and are harsh to the touch. The stems (inset, Text Fig. 486) are hollow, jointed, and ridged. At each

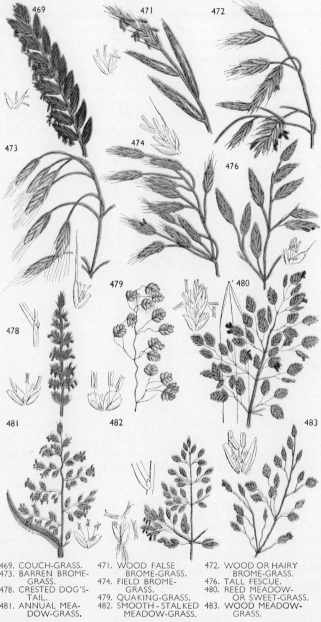

469. COUCH-GRASS.
473. BARREN BROME-
        GRASS.
478. CRESTED DOG'S-
        TAIL.
481. ANNUAL MEA-
        DOW-GRASS.

471. WOOD FALSE
        BROME-GRASS.
474. FIELD BROME-
        GRASS.
479. QUAKING-GRASS.
482. SMOOTH - STALKED
        MEADOW-GRASS.

472. WOOD OR HAIRY
        BROME-GRASS.
476. TALL FESCUE.
480. REED MEADOW-
        OR SWEET-GRASS.
483. WOOD MEADOW-
        GRASS.

joint there is a toothed sheath enclosing the next stem-section. The stems are either unbranched or bear whorls of branches at the joints. The spores are enclosed by brown or black scales in an oval or oblong spike at the end of the stem (Fig. 487). Some species have separate barren and fruiting stems, which may vary in structure, and may appear together or at different times. They are variable plants. As all these factors must be considered, the identification of the dozen or so British species is often difficult. The following are perhaps the two most likely to be found. The fruiting season is given.

486. FIELD HORSETAIL, *Equisétum arvénse, of cultivated fields*. Spring.

Fruiting stem thick, brownish, about 9 in. high, simple, in spring, dying before the slenderly branched green barren stems, from 1 ft. to 2 ft. high, arise. Of fields and waste places, particularly if moist. A bad weed, difficult to eradicate owing to its very deep, spreading root-stock. Considered poisonous to stock (Text Fig. 486).

487. MARSH HORSETAIL, *Equisétum palústre, of marshes*. Summer.

Fruiting and barren stems similar, from 1 ft. to 1½ ft. high. Branches, not many, in a whorl, rather short and thick. Of marshes and bogs. Name from Latin *equus*, horse, and *seta*, bristle. The plants have many local names.

FERN FAMILIES: *Filices*

Ferns are widely spread over the world, being particularly, but not invariably, associated with moist climates and situations. Some exotic species have tall, woody, tree-like stems. They are not of great economic value, but at times have been extremely popular as cultivated plants.

In Britain, most are perennial herbs with tufted or creeping root-stocks. The combined stem and leaves, structurally different from the similar parts of a flowering plant, are called the frond. These are frequently rolled up when young. In many kinds the underside of the frond bears numerous *sori* (inset *so*, Text Fig. 491), generally brownish in colour, which each consist of a cluster of little cases containing the minute *spores*, produced without any process of flowering or fertilization, from which, when liberated and carried by the wind to a suitable spot, the young ferns will be produced. In some kinds the spores are borne on the edges of the fronds, and in others, on separate spikes at the end of the fronds. The method of carrying the spores, and the arrangement and structure of the sori, are important points in identify, ing ferns.

Some species produce many varieties, often with crested and remark, ably formed fronds. These were formerly widely cultivated.

A spore, settled in an appropriate spot for its germination, develops into a small green scale-like sort of plantlet called a *prothállus*. This bears on its underside, held close to the ground by rootlets, two separate sets of bodies, one of which may be called female, including an un, fertilized seed at its base, and the other male, containing a minute hairy object called an *antherozoíd*. Under certain rather precise conditions of moisture and temperature, this antherozoid is liberated and swims in a spot of moisture, by means of its hairs, to the incipient seed, which it fertilizes, and from which grows the young fern. It should be mentioned that ferns have also other methods of reproduction, but this is the usual life-cycle.

The seasons following the name are those in which the fructification is fully developed.

ROYAL FERN FAMILY: *Osmundáceae*

Limited in Britain to the following:

488. ROYAL or FLOWERING FERN, *Osmúnda regális, royal*. Late summer to autumn.

Fronds growing in tufts, varying according to situation and climate from 2 ft. to 10 ft. high. The spore-cases are clustered together in a sort of panicle at the end of a frond (inset *a*, Text Fig. 488), having the appearance of a flower-stem, hence the descriptive but botanically wrong name 'flowering fern.' A very handsome plant, mostly found in the moist counties of the W., but frequently planted by water-sides in gardens. Named after Thor (*Osmunder*) (Text Fig. 488).

POLYPODY FAMILY: *Polypodiáceae*

To this belong most British ferns.

489. COMMON POLYPODY, *Polypódium vulgáre, common*. Summer to autumn.

Rootstock thick and creeping. Fronds 6 in. to 1½ ft. Sori golden-yellow. Of walls, moist rocks, hedgerows, and similar situations. Forms with peculiar branching and lobing are found, and often cultivated. Name from Greek *polus*, many, and *pous*, foot, from the numerous fronds borne by some kinds.

490. PRICKLY SHIELDFERN, *Aspidium aculeátum, prickly.* Summer to autumn.

Fronds tufted, from 1 ft. to 3 ft. high, stiff; segments prickly. Hedge-banks and similar shady places.

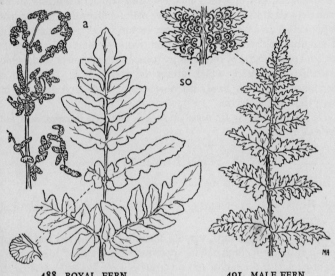

488. ROYAL FERN   491. MALE FERN

491. MALE FERN, *Aspidium Fílix-mas.* Summer to autumn.

Fronds in a large circular tuft, handsome, stiff and erect. One of the commonest ferns, producing numerous varieties which are found in gardens. Of woods and shady places. Oil of male fern, made from the rootstock, has long been an important vermifuge (Text Fig. 491, inset *so*, showing sori).

492. BROAD SHIELDFERN, *Aspidium spinulósum, with small spines.* Summer to autumn.

Rather similar to the male fern, but generally broader and shorter, up to 2 ft. high, and paler green. The fronds are more divided. Of damp, open woods and similar sheltered places. Numerous varieties

are found and many cultivated. Name from Greek *aspis*, a shield,
from the shape of the covering of the sori.

493. LADY FERN, *Asplénium Fílix-foémina*.   Summer to autumn.

A more delicate and elegant version of the male fern in general
appearance and habit. (*Male* and *lady* were originally applied because
of their general similarity yet different qualities.) Easily distinguished

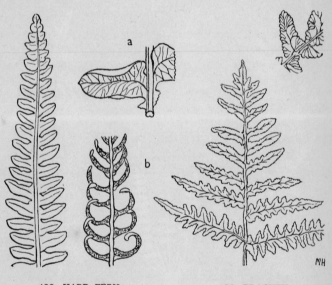

499. HARD FERN	500. BRACKEN

by the elongated sori. Numerous varieties are found. Of moist woods
and sheltered, shady places.

494. COMMON or WALL SPLEENWORT, *Asplénium Trichómanes*.
     Spring to autumn.

A small tufted fern, 6 in. high or smaller. Stem almost black.
Of walls and rocks.

495. BLACK SPLEENWORT, *Asplénium Adiántum-nígrum*.   Summer to
     autumn.

Fronds tufted, with a long dark-coloured stalk. Sori near mid-
vein, 3 in. to 1 ft. high. Walls and hedge-banks.

484. PURPLE MELICK-
    GRASS.
489. COMMON POLY-
    PODY.
493. LADY FERN.
496. WALL RUE.

485. COMMON REED.
490. PRICKLY SHIELD-
    FERN.
494. COMMON OR
    WALL SPLEEN-
    WORT.
497. HART'S-TONGUE.

487. MARSH HORSE-
    TAIL.
492. BROAD SHIELD-
    FERN.
495. BLACK SPLEEN-
    WORT.
498. RUSTY-BACK.

96. WALL RUE, *Asplénium Rúta-murária.* Spring to early autumn.

Fronds densely tufted, only an inch or two long. Sori linear or in atches. Of old walls and rocks. Rare in some eastern counties.

97. HART'S-TONGUE, *Scolopéndrium vulgáre, common.* Summer.

Fronds tufted and entire, about 1 ft. long but sometimes much more. ori in parallel rows on the underside. Variable, producing some riking crested forms. Of shady banks, rocky places, and old walls.

98. RUSTY-BACK, SCALY SPLEENWORT, *Cetérach officinárium, used by man.* Summer to autumn.

Fronds tufted, deeply lobed, green on the upper side, densely covered ith brown scales underneath which usually hide the sori. Of old alls and rocks, particularly in Ireland and the W. side of Britain id Scotland.

99. HARD FERN, *Bléchnum Spícant.* Late summer.

Fronds tufted from 6 in. to 1 ft. high, of two kinds: the outer shorter, preading, and barren (Text Fig. 499, and inset *a*, from under); the iner more upright, comb-like, and fruiting (inset *b*, from under). Of oods and heaths in moist situations.

00. BRACKEN, *Pterídium aquilínum, eagle-like.* Autumn.

An erect plant with a vigorously creeping rootstock. Fronds twice thrice pinnate, from 1 ft. to 10 ft. high according to situation. Voods, heaths, waste places, and often an invasive and troublesome veed in upland pastures, though useful as bedding for stock and cover r game. It is poisonous in varying degree to cattle and game (Text ig. 500).

INDEX

Botanical terms are printed in italics without a capital initial,
and are defined on the page given.